Other books by Iris Angellys

Passion to Thrive: Reclaim Your Life's Potential, Purpose, Passion and Power

your
body is the
portal to your
 soul

Contents

Algorithm or Humanity? **153**

Forward

Iris and I have worked in the same field for over 17 years together and in that time, I have seen her talents, abilities and therefore her own spiritual awareness grow, shift and blossom in beautiful ways. Her love and care for her patients and also for humanity knows no bounds and her desire to shift the consciousness of the world around her is quite inspiring. This is her second book in what I hope is a long string of books to help shape and expand our understanding of ourselves. She helps us to recognise how precious each and every one of us is, not only for our own self-worth but also for our role within the greater community that is planet Earth.

As a fellow healer who has helped thousands of people in their journeys, I love and identify so strongly with Iris' descriptions of how energy flows and how it is the main cause of disease and lack of thriving for humans. Her explanations on how to process emotions, and how to identify and work with the body gives us some really simple guidelines to follow and practical tools to keep that energy and therefore health and vitality flowing. If we can learn to go within to honour ourselves rather than using external loci of identity, often losing ourselves in the crowd, we can truly learn what deep internal happiness is all about.

I deeply respect Iris's work and her commitment to health and wellbeing. She is a person who walks her talk (a rare thing), and that integrity is shown in the conviction of her words in this book. To be deeply healthy within and without is a rare gift we can give ourselves and we all need a bit of Iris in our life.

Kate Connolly,
Owner and Principal Practitioner of Natural Health Works,
and Author of "*The Intuitive Heart Revolution*"
https://www.kateconnolly.com.au

Introduction

Most humans have a fraught relationship with their bodies. They believe they aren't slim enough, young enough or wrinkle-free enough. Their belly, bum, thighs or shoulders are too big or too small. They feel too tired, not sexy enough and so on. Many companies make big profits from people feeling physically inadequate and insecure. These companies actively encourage this mindset by continuously showing us airbrushed images of exceptionally beautiful people.

As a result, we hate our bodies, or treat them harshly with exercise, chemicals or even surgery to make them live up to this image we have of our ideal physical self. We force our bodies to feel a particular way with excessive exercise, dieting and prescription or 'recreational' drugs. Or we flee our physical world altogether by losing ourselves in our screens.

We feel angry, betrayed and hurt when our bodies stop working the way we feel they should, start hurting or get sick.

We have forgotten how to listen to our bodies and understand the signals they give us about what they need to thrive. Most people do not know what it feels like to feel good in their bodies.

This mindset does not serve us at all.

Read on to explore how we can rediscover our bodies' messages and create a relationship of respect, joy, caring and love with our bodies.

Relearn just how powerful we can be.

And, if you would like to deepen your connection and communication to your body, come on over to my website irisangellys.com where I have all sorts of additional resources to guide you through all the practical aspects in an easy and explorative way.

Why I wrote this book – and why you should read it

In my work as a chiropractor and applied kinesiologist, I have gained a deep understanding of how bodies work. They always have a reason for doing what they do. Bodies want to feel vibrantly alive!

Most people have no idea how their bodies work or how to understand the signals they receive from their bodies. Most people, in fact, feel terrible and aren't even aware of it.

In this book, I give you the keys to change how you interact with your body so that you can feel good both in and about your body.

Everything in this book is based on experience, my own and my patients', so I know it works.

I offer a lot of strategies in this book on how to nurture your body and rekindle your relationship with it. Start by picking one or two that appeal to you and feel easy to implement.

Once you have integrated one action, move on to the next one. Change is easiest if done little by little. If you try to do everything at once, you're likely to set yourself up for overwhelm. Understand there is a reason for your current choices in how you live your life, and that the best way to change direction is with gentle, sustainable shifts, not abrupt overhauls.

love rather than need?

When you believe that all you have to offer the world is your possessions, or your status, or the roles you play, or your body, you become dependent on facets outside of who you truly are.

Paradoxically, everybody who loves you knows there is far more to you than meets the eye. Do you?

You are not your possessions

This sounds obvious, but many people identify with their possessions and derive their worth from them.

This can look like:

"I am the owner of the biggest, most luxurious and most expensive house/ yacht/ car/ jewels/second, third, or fourth homes..."

How do you know if you identify with your possessions? When you lose them, you try frantically to replace them. Without them, you no longer know how to move in the world. You no longer know who you are.

If you don't identify with the possession, you can think to yourself, "Ah well, it was nice to own it while it lasted."

This can work in reverse too. If you identify with being poor, living hand to mouth, and not belonging to anyone or anything, and you do end up with some money or other abundance, you are likely to lose it, give it away or squander it in the blink of an eye.

If you don't identify with owning nothing, you are likely to live a comfortably abundant life.

Who are you without your possessions?

You are not your body

Many people derive identity from their bodies, be they beautiful, ugly, skinny, fat, muscular, black, white, brown, disabled, athletic, female, male, or somewhere in the middle. Many people have beliefs about what those qualities and characteristics mean. This is held so tightly in our societies that it becomes a reality for a lot of people.

For example, if you are tall and beautiful, you are treated differently from someone who is short and plain.

But living a life of self-confidence and self-worth with beautiful, meaningful, loving relationships does not depend on being tall and beautiful.

You will have both pleasant and unpleasant physical experiences during your stay on planet Earth, some of which will be based on what your body looks like. Your body can carry out some actions and not others which will colour your experience of your life.

The one certainty in life is you will live with your body for the entire length of your stay on planet Earth.

Your body is your exquisite time-space travelling companion, without which you cannot experience life on Earth.

Who are you when you are not your body?

You are not the roles you play

Identifying with the roles we play happens all the time.

When you are introduced to someone, you are first told their name. Second, you usually find out their occupation. "Hello, my name is John Smith. I am an emergency doctor", engenders a different mindset and level of interest than "Hello, my name is

Bliss
Playfulness
Delight
Freedom
Love
Gratitude
Acceptance
Stillness
Creativity
Curiosity
Love
Care
Beauty
Nurture
Infinity
Love
Generosity
Communion
Compassion
Community
Love
Abundance
Courage
Richness
Harmony
Balance
Love
Love
Love

"We are mosaics. Pieces of light, love, history, stars…glued together with magic and music and words."

—Anita Krizzan

WHAT IS YOUR BODY?

When you think about it, Life is unlikely. Here we are, a spirit of pure love, inhabiting a physical body on a tiny planet spinning around an average star in an average galaxy hurtling through the infinite space of the universe.

First, let's look at what your body isn't.

Your body is not a machine

We have been trained to think of our bodies as a collection of parts, each functioning independently of the other. But you cannot change or affect one part without having an effect on all the other parts.

Western medicine tends to go into more and more detail, forgetting about the whole that all these details are part of. You can smash a cup and describe a shard, or analyse the substance it was made of, but this will tell you nothing about what a cup looks like or how it functions when it is whole.

There are three systems in the body so pervasive and fine that you would   recognise a loved one if you only saw these parts of them. Don't think of these as you would see them on an anatomy chart, but imagine a statue made of these systems rather than of clay or stone.

∞ The blood supply: every cell in the body needs blood. The smallest blood vessels, the capillaries, are so tiny they only let one red blood cell through at a time. They are so densely distributed and pervasive because every single cell in the body needs to be fed by the blood and have its waste taken away.

∞ The nervous system: the brain and spinal cord control, coordinate and receive information about the function of all cells, organs and systems in the body via the nerves that emerge from the spine. They are as densely and extensively distributed as the blood vessels.

∞ The fascia: this connective tissue holds everything in place both on a micro (cellular) and on a macro level. For example, the big tendon down the outside of your thigh, the fascia lata, is a fascial structure. Fascia is a three-dimensional web that connects everything and holds it together.

The blood vessels, nerves and fascia allow the cells in the body to communicate in different ways. It does not matter how remote the cells are from each other.

The upshot of this is *you **cannot** do something to one part of the body without the whole rest of the body knowing about it.* The *whole body* somehow ***has*** to adapt to or deal with it. Or benefit from it.

If you have an operation and you get a scar, the scar changes the fascial pull on the rest of the body's fascia, like lines in cling film that has been pulled. If you have an angry thought, your body goes into fight-or-flight mode. If you take a medicine, this medicine interacts with and potentially affects all the cells in your body.

Likewise, if you do a type of body movement that gives you joy, your whole body feels better for it. If you eat a nourishing food, your whole body feels better for it. If you allow yourself to enjoy rest, your whole body feels better for it.

Our bodies are integrated entities. Every single cell, organ and system is affected by every other cell, organ and system. Each cell, organ and system has its own exquisite role to play in the wellbeing of the whole body. If one part of the body does not fulfill its role, the whole body is affected by this. The body is self-healing but does not come with spare parts.

You can understand and describe the body in many ways. You may find some of the following concepts foreign, but if you resonate with one or two of them and start to interact with your body in this new way, it will open up a whole new way to interact, experience, understand and nurture your body.

Your body is an expression of nature

We are spiritual beings inhabiting a physical body.

The physical body itself belongs to nature. It is a being, like a little animal. It has its own innate intelligence that knows what it needs to survive and to thrive.

If you don't act on your body's guidance, you are using up tomorrow's energy today. Your body will need you to pay it back with interest. For example, if you don't get enough sleep, you feel groggy for a couple of days. If you have coffee every day to counteract it, you feel groggy your whole life. If you drink to excess one night, you feel hungover the next day. If you take medicine to counteract it in the morning, and drink again that same night, you feel hungover your whole life.

The basics our bodies need to thrive are good food, water, rest, exercise, sunshine, time in nature, and affection. If you have a cherished pet, do you ensure these basics are met? Most devoted pet owners wouldn't dream of mistreating their animal companion by depriving it of any one of these necessities. For this reason, I encourage you to think of your body as a cherished pet, a little animal that tells you exactly what it needs and when.

If you truly give your body what it needs, your body feels good and thrives! When you feel good in your body, you have the freedom to do whatever else your soul yearns to do while it is visiting Earth.

Think of this like a horse and rider. You, a spirit of pure love experiencing humanness, are the rider, and the horse is your body. Your horse will take you from A to B, provided you tend it kindly and well enough not to get bucked off.

However, imagine how much more delightful the ride is when you care for your horse like a friend, giving it nourishing food, clear water, and lots of love and affection. Your horse feels wonderful and strong and loved. This horse looks out for you, makes sure you don't fall off, and finds its way home if you happen to fall asleep while you are out riding. Our bodies are just like that.

Your body is a chemical symphony

Innumerable biochemical events happen in your body every moment of your life. A phenomenal symphony of processes takes place that you don't even have to think about. Every cell knows exactly what to do to thrive and to help the rest of the body to thrive.

Each cell needs raw materials which are provided by the air we breathe, the water we drink and the food we eat. Sadly, these days it is hard to find air, water and food free from pollution. Pollution consists of chemicals and radiation the body doesn't need but must still process and eliminate, which takes up extra resources.

You can make smart choices about how you nourish yourself. If you eat pre-prepared food, a whole host of chemicals are likely to have been added to give it texture, flavour and a long shelf-life. This adds polluting chemicals for your body to deal with, which uses up valuable resources, while at the same time not providing useful nutrients. This sets you up for a vicious cycle of feeling flat, making quick-fix food choices, and feeling even worse as a consequence.

The answer is to choose foods still in the state nature offered them. Preparing a meal from scratch is neither particularly hard nor time-consuming. It is also an opportunity to express creativity. And, believe it or not, if you prepare food with loving intent, it will nourish you more.

Molecules of emotion

Dr Candace Pert wrote a book called "Molecules of Emotion". In it, she describes her discovery that each emotion, such as anger, sadness, joy, guilt or love, is communicated through biochemical messengers called neurotransmitters. Each cell has receptors for these molecules, and when the molecules connect with the receptors, the cell knows what's going on with the whole body. For example, the body, and hence the cell, can understand if it is in flight-or-fight mode or rest-or-digest mode.

The emotions we engage with habitually and most frequently, induce the cells to create more receptors to respond to these particular emotions. It is the same mechanism for substance addictions. You experience withdrawals both for substances and for emotions when these receptors aren't getting their expected 'fix' of molecules.

By the age of 35, we have experienced the whole range of possible human emotions and have settled on a particular baseline. This means we have found our basic way of being in the world: happy, depressed, thrill-seeking, angry, anxious, curious and so on. If these receptors are left unstimulated, the cells suffer withdrawal symptoms. In response, we seek something in our outer environment to justify feeling this way again, thus feeding our cells' emotion receptors. This is why resilient people bounce back from adversity really well. It is why pessimists find a problem for every solution, and why some people are always angry.

This baseline has a profound influence on our mental wellbeing, but it is also crucial for our physical wellbeing. It tends to keep our bodies in either fight-or-flight (stress) or in rest-and-repair (thrive) mode. Our bodies are unable to thrive if they are perpetually in fight-or-flight, which eventually leads to physical symptoms.

"The moment you change your perception is the moment you rewrite the chemistry in your body."

—Bruce Lipton

Your body is a liquid crystal

Our bodies consist of about two-thirds water. Water is the second most important nutrient for our bodies after air. Water is the substrate that allows all the functions of our body to happen.

If you have come across the sage Masaru Emoto's work, you know that different frequencies, such as words, music and concepts, affect water in different ways. Low frequency concepts, such as "You fool!", create disorganisation within the structure of water. High frequency concepts, like love and peace, create beautifully shaped water crystals. Think of them as snowflakes within the liquid.

If water is in a crystal shape, it conducts energy well. If the water molecules in your body are resonating with higher frequency concepts, they can conduct energy more readily. If you are in distress, the water molecules become disorganised, and the energy is likely to get stuck in your body. The cells in your body have a harder time functioning well, because they rely on water to conduct the electricity they generate to function.

The water molecules in your body react to everything you do, think and experience. Every thought or emotion you have affects the structure of the water inside you. Everything you consume affects the water molecules inside you.

The good news is that it is up to you what you think, how you process your emotions, and what you consume.

Bless the water you are about to drink. It will nourish your body more deeply.

Check out Dr. Masaru Emoto's website
emotopeaceproject.net/water-crystal-gallery

Your body is a community

A human body might seem like a discrete entity, but each one is composed of trillions of individual cells. These cells are individuals that do what they were created to do to sustain their own lives as well as the life of the body as a whole. Each cell contributes to the survival and thriving of the body.

Each cell keeps constantly informed about what the body is experiencing through the blood supply, nerve supply, fascia and hormones. Each cell is bathed in the molecules of emotion that you secrete in response to what's going on for you, both internally and externally.

And each of these cells do the best they can under the circumstances. If cells act in a dysfunctional way, it is because they do not have the resources they need to thrive. They start sending distress signals to the wider organism about their discomfort. These signals appear as symptoms.

If you pay attention and give your body what it needs when it needs it, your body feels well and happy.

If you ignore the signals or suppress the symptoms in some way, such as with prescription or recreational drugs, alcohol, coffee, excessive exercise, screen use, etc., you drive the dysfunction deeper, and it eventually develops into dis-ease and sickness. It's like covering up the light on the dashboard that lets you know you need fuel and then wondering why your car grinds to a halt on the highway.

"You may consider yourself an individual. But as a cell biologist I can tell you that you are in truth a cooperative community of approximately fifty trillion single-celled citizens."

—Bruce Lipton

Your body is a cell in the body of humanity

Just like everyone's individual bodies are made up of trillions of cells, your body is part of the organism called humanity. Just like the cells in our body, we each have a function to fulfill within humanity. This function or purpose is generally what you love doing, whatever makes your heart sing with joy.

Each and every function is important. A liver cell doesn't think it's better than a nerve cell. They have different purposes, and your body needs both types. In the same way, the whole of humanity needs each and every human to do what they love, to offer their unique gift and to thrive.

If you take a step towards remembering your own true nature, if you take a step towards health, if you take a step away from anger or jealousy or conflict, you are progressing all of humanity by creating the consciousness in the collective that this is possible.

Ubuntu is a Zulu word that means "If you are not ok, I am not ok." It says we are all connected in our shared humanity, and for one to thrive, all must thrive.

Ubuntu is a philosophy of African tribes
that can be summed up as:
"I am because we are."
"A person is a person through
other people."

—Source unknown, Ubuntu Philosophy

Your body is a cell in the body of Earth

Your body is part of the ecosystem. You are welcome to take what you need to feed your life so you can thrive. You are also required to contribute in alignment with your own true nature. This is how nature works. Every single cell, creature, mineral, plant, bacterium, virus, animal, and human meets their needs and contributes   to the wellbeing of the whole.

I remember being introduced to the concept of humans' purpose being to 'tend the garden'. I take that to mean we approach everything we get to experience with an intention of nurture and with a sense of gratitude.

When you eat, be grateful to the food nourishing your body. When you drink water, be grateful for the wellbeing the water gives your body.

And when you do something, do it with a sense of contributing your unique, beautiful frequency to whatever you are doing.

Your body is a feedback entity

On one level, the body lets us know what it needs to feel well, happy, healthy and whole.

On another level, the body gives us physical sensations in response to our emotions, such as butterflies in the stomach when we see the one we are in love with, or warmth in the heart when we hug someone we love, or coldness in the belly when we feel fear, or tightness in the shoulders when we are stressed and anxious.

Not only does the body signal what it needs to thrive for itself, it also signals what you, as the being who lives in the body, need to thrive.

The feedback we get from our body is not random. Each part of our body has a separate function that serves as a metaphor when it is communicating with us through symptoms. The body part draws our attention to the energy we are oblivious to in this way. It is no accident that we use terms like 'pisses me off', 'pain in the neck', 'that's short-sighted', 'I can't stomach that', etc.

For example, the large intestine is about letting go easily and effortlessly when it's time to do so. If you have trouble letting go, whether it is too much or not often enough, this might be drawn to your attention with irritable bowel syndrome.

Women are blessed with an inbuilt feedback system in the form of menstruation once a month. If we go with the flow of our body's changes and different requirements each month, having a period is no big deal. If we compromise ourselves during the month, it is likely to come out as irritability or pre-menstrual syndrome. Maybe, if we give too much, we bleed too much. If we do not embrace our femininity, we might not bleed at all. If we dislike being female, we might have a lot of pain during menstruation.

These metaphors are different for everyone. I invite you to notice what language you use to describe your physical discomforts. This is the key that can unlock what Life is asking you to integrate.

Numerous books have been written to interpret what the body is drawing your attention to, the most famous probably being the pioneering, "*You Can Heal Your Life*" by Louise Hay.

Your body is an energy field

I am sure you know the equation $E=mc^2$. It means that matter is really, really slow energy. Or that if you speed matter up by the speed of light times the speed of light, you end up with energy. In other words, energy and matter are the same, the difference is the speed at which the energy moves. Matter is congealed energy so to speak.

As an analogy, if you put a glass of water in the freezer, you get a thin layer of ice on the top to start with. The water in the lower part of the glass stays fluid for longer. Your body is like the ice in your glass of water. It is the densest part of your energy field, except that it's in the middle of the energy field, rather than on the surface.

Your body is also, according to this equation, a creature of energy, light and information making up the atoms and molecules of your tissues.

We have been taught our beings are contained within the body. Yet each of our energy fields are many times larger than the body. They contain and include the body.

Your energy field and body are intimately connected, fluidly intertwined.

When an energy comes into your awareness, such as a thought, emotion, concept or habit, you feel it in your energy field first. If the energy is not processed, it gets stuck in your energy field, growing denser and denser, until it shows up as a physical sensation and potentially a disease.

Your energy field is better at processing energy than your physical body, and thus can protect your body. In our societies, we are taught that the body contains the energy field, and because energy follows thought, this ends up being true, leaving the body vulnerable.

Your body is a light entity

When we say someone is bright, this is quite accurate. Bodies emit photons, units of light.

Sunlight is our source of the full spectrum of light. Yet, most of us subject our bodies to 'junk light', or artificial light, most of the time. As a result, we do not experience the full light spectrum that sunlight provides.

The blue part of the spectrum, which LED lights and screens emit, stimulates the brain, whereas the red part of the light spectrum calms it down. It would do our bodies the world of good if we went back to candles and firelight after dark. We'd have deeper, more restorative sleep.

Sunlight feels good! Our bodies crave it. I invite you to consciously take in the light of a sunrise or a sunset and notice how different your energy field feels as a result. This is not an invitation to get sunburnt. Listen to your body when it tells you that it has had enough sun as well.

Your body is your time-space suit

You are a spark of Divine Consciousness, a spiritual being of pure love. Dropping into the physical body of a human being, also made of energy, allows you to experience three-dimensional physical reality, which is made of energy as well. This amazing illusion allows you to experience yourself as separate from the Whole, even though it is all energy.

Your body is your unique, miraculous vehicle that enables you to live Life in physical reality. It is perfectly equipped to guide you through this life. It provides you with the ability to meander through time and space, and explore, sense and experience everything!

Your body is also your precious tool to express your unique frequency, vibration, gifts and love, without which creation would not be complete.

Your body as an integrated entity

Our bodies are all these aspects all at the same time. Each aspect affects all the other aspects.

For example, if your energy is high, your posture is tall and you breathe easily and fully, energising your whole body with ease and grace.

If you are weighed down by heavy emotions or thoughts, your posture reflects this by shrinking in on itself with a slumping spine and shoulders. This, in turn, makes breathing harder and requires more energy to deal with gravity's pull.

If you feel down, put a smile on your face. Even if you're 'faking it till you make it', your brain receives the message that there is something to smile about. Soon the smile feels genuine. You find a new perspective on what was bothering you and before you know it, your whole body stands up tall, resonating with joy.

If you eat or drink something incompatible with a healthy body, you end up with a hangover or upset gut. You feel grumpy.

If you nourish yourself with poor-quality food, drink and movement, your body might need to use minerals, such as the calcium stored in your bones, to counteract their effects. You could end up with osteoporosis.

I have noticed most of us have a time, usually around a birthday with a zero at the end of it, where we think we are 'old'. When we reach this age, the body follows instructions and starts falling apart.

How about we start talking nicely to our bodies instead?

How about we start interacting our bodies as a miraculous, intelligent and precious entity?

Your body is your best friend for life!

The *only* being you are absolutely guaranteed to spend your whole life with is your body. Your body loves you in the same way you love nature, or God, or the starry night sky. Your body wants to have a loving relationship with you. Your body wants to thrive, feel happy and go on adventures with you.

You might as well make your body your friend. Love your body back and care for it with wonder and gratitude. It isn't all that hard. Your experience of Life will be so much richer and enjoyable for it.

Practice
Self-reflection

How do you feel about your body now?

Knowing what you know now about how interconnected and multifaceted and miraculous your body is, reflect on the following:

- ∞ *What do you tell your body on a daily basis?*
- ∞ *What do you tell the cells that are doing their best to be healthy and do a good job for the sake of the community that is your body?*
- ∞ *How many ways do you tell your body it is deficient or ugly? Or do you tell your body how wonderful and amazing it is?*
- ∞ *Do you tell it what a wonderful travelling companion it is through this wild ride we call life?*
- ∞ *How can you talk nicely to your body?*
- ∞ *How can you interact with your body as if it is a miraculous, intelligent and precious entity?*

"Today I asked my body what she needed,
Which is a big deal
Considering my journey of
Not really asking that much.

I thought she might need more water.
Or proteins.
Or greens.
Or yoga.
Or supplements.
Or movement.

But as I stood in the shower
Reflecting on her stretch marks,
Her roundness where I would like flatness,
Her softness where I would prefer firmness,
All those conditioned wishes
That form a bundle of
Never-Quite-Right-Ness,
She whispered very gently:

Could you just love me like this?"

—Hollie Holden

The Purpose of Life

The purpose of Life
Is just to be gloriously, vibrantly, radiantly alive!
Experiencing everything
Resisting nothing
Feeling into the depths and widths of breadths of what it means to be human

The purpose of Life
Is to embrace everything it means to be human
While remembering that we are beings of Divine Breath
And stardust

The purpose of Life
Is to see Beauty
In all other Beings
Human, animal, plant, mineral, ethereal, the planet Herself
Even when it isn't pretty

The purpose of Life
Is to remember our shared humanity
Ubuntu
And to be curious about our differences

The purpose of Life
Is to see what connects us all
Heart to heart
Past the surface appearances of
What seems to separate us

The purpose of Life
Is to experience intensely through our senses
The taste of mangoes
The colours of a sunset
The softness of skin
The resonance of beautiful music
And allow it to nurture our soul
And our body
In equal measure

The purpose of Life
Is to celebrate the magic
Of Simple Things
Like cooking a delicious meal
Laughter with friends
Hugs with the ones we love

The purpose of Life
Is to look deeply into Another's eyes
To remind them of their own Divine connection
When they have lost their sense of who they really are

The purpose of Life
Is to sing our unique song with wild abandon
To shine our beautiful, precious
Frequency
Into the Universe

The purpose of Life
Is to live in awe
Of the miracle of being alive
A spirit of pure Love inhabiting a human body
Breath bridging the physical with the Unseen

The purpose of Life
Is for Source to see
And celebrate
Itself
Through our eyes

The purpose of Life
Is Love

YOUR GUIDANCE SYSTEMS

The trick with your guidance systems is to listen to the first 'reply' or impulse that comes to you. This can be a word or sentence that sounds like your own voice. It can be a feeling in your body. It can be a knowingness. It can be a visual impression, or a combination of all the above. It generally has a quiet, still and clear feeling to it.

The mind often jumps in a split second later, with opinions, judgements, justifications or interpretations based on what someone once said or did. This is generally a loud, chaotic, contradictory and complex voice.

Practice noticing that first impulse. It gets easier the more you use it.

You can also:

- ∞ Put your hand on your heart.
- ∞ Take a big breath.
- ∞ Ask your heart the question again.
- ∞ Tune into what your guidance system says as you breathe out.

Two occasions taught me why it is so important to follow my guidance.

When I was 12 years old, I was out and about on horseback on my own one day. I came across some people out in the countryside who felt scary to me. I think they might have thrown stones at us. I sped the horse up to get away in a hurry.

Walking home from the stables, I had the option of walking

along the creek or walking along the roads. I had this sense that I should walk along the roads but overrode it as being nonsensical because the path along the creek, away from houses, was more pleasant.

As I walked along the creek, I came across those same people. I had to run to get away from them.

The second occasion was when I was 16. I agreed to keep some cats company while their humans were away on holiday. The cats lived in a house on the other side of town, probably a good 45-minute bike ride away. I had a bad feeling about going and didn't for a couple of days. My mother eventually reminded me that I had committed to these cats, so off I went.

As I was riding along on my bicycle, I saw a band of around 15 boys riding along on their bikes. I chose a different path, but I encountered them again later, on a different road. They swarmed me and grabbed at me. I was enraged and terrified. I eventually managed to turn around and make my escape.

These are examples of getting clear inner guidance and then overriding it with the mind. I had no objective way of knowing about these dangers, but my sixth sense warned me. These days, if I get a feeling to do something different, I trust it. I don't want to know what might happen if I take the mind-based option.

Your body's guidance about what it needs

Your body is of the Earth. It is uniquely qualified to guide you on how to look after it so it can thrive, and you can thrive, while on the Earthplane.

The body has some basic requirements: food, water, exercise, sunshine, affection and rest.

An easy way to find out what and how much your body needs is to tune into questions like:

- ∞ Does it make your body feel good?
- ∞ Does it make your body feel vital and intensely alive?
- ∞ Does it make you feel joy in your body?

A subtle distinction arises here. For example, if you tend to abuse a substance such as alcohol, cigarettes, sugar or drugs, you might answer, "yes" to the first question above because it makes your mind or emotions feel good, at least for a moment.

But! Does your *body* feel good? How does your body feel after the drug has worn off? Does it feel hungover, lethargic, edgy, and generally unpleasant? *That* is your body's answer. The part that says, "yes" to abusing your body is the ego or mind, not the body.

A buzz or high is quite different to sustainable vitality and radiant health.

It saddens me that most people don't know what it means to feel good in their bodies. Anybody who is uncomfortably overweight, arthritic, continuously tired, stressed or 'officially sick' does not feel good. Categorically!

My body does not like gluten or dairy. For years, I felt constantly tired. I thought it was normal to feel lethargic after eating. Then a friend and fellow practitioner told me to stop eating gluten, and the veil of brain-fog and tiredness lifted. If I eat gluten now, I get a migraine, irritability and lethargy one or two days after. When I eat what my body requires, the food makes my body feel energised.

If this has sparked something in you, I encourage you to see a naturopathic practitioner. They can arrange a test to find out what foods your body reacts to. Foods generally considered healthy can be foods your body reacts to idiosyncratically.

If your body needs water, drinking water feels like refuelling and the water tastes sweet.

Both rest and exercise can be addictive. Ask your body:

- ∞ Has my body had enough rest? Does my body need to move now?
- ∞ Has my body moved enough? Does it need to rest?

A little phrase shows up in my head that is invariably a signal I am about to ignore my body's needs: "I'll just…"

Prime examples include working on the computer and starting to feel tired. I often think "I'll just get this done…" Getting it done usually takes a lot longer than the 10 minutes I think it should. By the time the task is completed, I am exhausted. If I follow my body's guidance instead, and take a spell, I gain a whole new lease on life and get the task completed within the anticipated 10 minutes.

Bargaining with your body

In my work as a healthcare professional, it is not unusual for me to encounter someone who says, "I know I shouldn't eat junk food and drink soft drinks, but I exercise" or "I know I don't get enough sleep, but I eat well" or "I know I shouldn't smoke, but I drink lots of water."

This is a bit like saying "I put premium petrol in my car, but I don't do oil changes or get new tyres."

Where did we get this idea that we can expect our bodies to be perfectly healthy and functioning despite not meeting all their essential needs? How did we end up in the situation where we think if we meet one need we are entitled to dismiss another? Our bodies need fuel *and* water *and* movement *and* rest *and* sunlight and so on. What we are doing in these instances is putting our bodies into deficit. We need to pay that energy back with interest in the following days. If we were talking about our pets, or even our vehicles, this would be a 'no-brainer'!

The usual mindset when our health starts to deteriorate is, "Ah well, I am getting old." While the march of time is inexorable, the health and wellbeing of someone who genuinely looks after their body is vastly different to that of someone who doesn't.

I encourage you to tune into your body's feedback. Your body is uniquely qualified to navigate life on Earth. If your body is thriving, feeling vital and exuberantly alive, you can thrive too.

Your emotions

Emotions are in the layer of the energy field closest to the body. They feel like sensations in, or just beyond, your body.

Some personal examples of how I experience different emotions are as follows:

- ∞ Fear feels like a clenched gut or constricted breath.
- ∞ Sadness and grief feel like a lump in my throat and tears in my eyes.
- ∞ Anger feels like the hackles standing up on my back (they probably do).
- ∞ Disappointment feels like a sinking feeling in my belly.
- ∞ Despair feels like tired numbness all over.
- ∞ Being broken up with feels like my energy field is shattering.
- ∞ Serenity feels like a deep, vast stillness in my core.
- ∞ Joy feels like expansion of my breath and tingling in my body.

∞ Excitement feels sparkly.

∞ Love feels like warmth in my chest.

∞ Compassion feels like a softening.

∞ Gratitude feels light in my chest with humble tears in my eyes.

∞ Confidence, feeling proud of myself and courage feel like a strong, erect back and open chest.

∞ Awe feels like a deep connection with whatever I am in awe of.

∞ Being proposed to feels like expansion, lightness and a whole new lifepath's worth of potential and possibilities.

A sense of light comes through in these emotions too. The 'down' or unpleasant emotions feel dark to me, whereas the 'up' or pleasant ones feel bright.

You might sense these emotions differently to me, such as different places in the body, different colours, different sensations, or even with different senses. I encourage you to notice these more subtle sensations in your body and name them.

If you can name the emotions accurately, you can perceive what your emotions are signalling to you more accurately. The more names you have, the more subtle and nuanced the feedback can be.

If you are good at identifying emotions, practice allowing the sensations to be there without naming them.

I once had a discussion with a man about emotions, and he told me, "Men are basic creatures. I really only know the basic emotions of angry, sad and happy." This is not the most useful way to be in the world.

For example, 'grief' is vastly different to 'despair', but if you don't know the difference and encounter 'despair', you won't know that you need to change your life radically compared to feeling grief when you mourn something that has ended.

If you don't know the difference between 'anger' and 'confidence', you might well come across as aggressive when you thought you were 'confident'. The world may seem unpredictable and strange when you can't finely tune into what feedback the energy moving through you is providing.

What emotions are trying to tell us

Joy, happiness, lightness, care and compassion let our hearts feel full and guide us to what gives our lives meaning. For most of us, these emotions don't cause too much trouble.

Sadness and grief let us know when we must let go of something, whether that be by our choice or not. Even if what is coming next is desired and anticipated with joy, something old must be let go of to make space for it. I will never forget this young lady who had yearned to become a mother for years. She was a couple of weeks away from giving birth to her first child when she told me a part of her was grieving that it would never again be just her and her husband. What an insightful young woman! In our society, expecting a baby is supposed to be all joy, without acknowledging the grief and other emotions that are a natural part of that process.

Shame and guilt let us know when we have sacrificed someone else's welfare for personal gain. They are essential for a functioning society. They are also known as remorse under those circumstances. It feels unpleasant and we know not to do it again.

In our current culture, shame has been twisted. We often learn from an early age that our mere existence is an imposition, that we are inherently wrong and that a whole life of atonement might not suffice to make up for the fact that we breathe. Some young children are told they are born in sin. All the potential and all the gifts this growing person could offer to the world are lost under this crippling lack of self-worth.

Despair and apathy are emotions that are one step away from death. They are the emotions you feel when you have reached your limits. These emotions tell you that you need to allow yourself time to heal, whatever that looks like for you at the time. You need to change what got you to this point in your life, once you have processed what went on.

Envy signals that someone else has, or is, what you desire for yourself. Jealousy lets you know you are feeling insecure in your relationship with a person.

Fear is a primal emotion that tells you if your physical life is in danger. Most of us are fortunate to never have to experience that. But because human beings are creatures that historically relied on the community for survival, you can also feel fear when your place in your community is threatened, or when you are in danger of being excluded from your social support. This kind of fear can have many flavours, including not being good enough, failing, succeeding, not being loveable, being rejected, being abandoned, not being needed. The list goes on. These kinds of fear make you easy to manipulate. When a human has a solid sense of their true inner worth, as opposed to worth gained from approval by others, they are hard to hoodwink.

Worry is a sign you care deeply. It is also an invitation to notice if you are being overly responsible, or even a rescuer, in this context.

Anger and rage are signs that your boundaries, or the boundaries of someone or something you care deeply about, have been crossed. When your physical, emotional, mental or spiritual integrity has been violated, anger and rage give you the energy and power to defend those boundaries and reclaim your sense of worth, integrity and safety. This is especially true if you stand up to someone who has some kind of power over you.

If you have a healthy relationship with anger, meaning you let the appropriate amount show in any given situation, people don't mess with you, and if they do, it doesn't take a whole lot of it to assert yourself. Many women are taught that being angry is not ok and that assertiveness in a woman is unattractive. That explains a lot, doesn't it!

Your intuition

This is the most subtle feedback system of all. It feels like movement in the energy field around you and in your body.

The most basic level of this is expansion and contraction or light and dark. Humans emit photons, or particles of light. What lights you up and makes you feel expansive, confident and excited, brightens and expands your energy field. If you are in a situation where you feel unsafe or compromised, you contract and dim your light.

You can connect with your intuition by noticing if the body is swaying towards something desirable or away from something undesirable. It can also feel like being in alignment or out of alignment, or the body feeling light or heavy. The pictures you see with your mind's eye can be bright and colourful or dark and grey.

"Intuition
When you don't know
How you know...
But you know you know...
and you know you knew
and that's all
you needed to know."

—Zen to Zany

Interviews with women about intuition

How does your intuition communicate with you?

Megan:

For as long as I can remember, I have experienced claircognisance, a clear knowing. I feel it in my whole being. I have a certainty I cannot logically explain. It is very black and white, a truth that brings tears to my eyes.

Over the years of connecting with my intuition and honouring the gift that it is, it has evolved from a knowing, to a feeling, a vision and a message from the soul and other realms. One of my favourite phrases is "show me what I need to see, hear, feel, know about my situation."

When I work with clients, I can tune into their emotional energy or that of a spirit around them.

I have a sense of awareness of where in their body the pain, trauma, resistance or fear is. I know how it needs to be released, what it needs to alchemize into and why the experience occurred in the first place.

I often draw diagrams which lead to words and create visions.

Beckie:

I feel my intuition in my body. It's what I call a whole-body yes or a whole-body no. It's a knowing felt deep within my bones, within my soul, and there's no questioning it when it's intuition. I used to get confused between anxiety and intuition when I struggled with chronic anxiety. They both felt the same to me. Because I questioned myself so much, I found it hard to know what was what.

Prue:

Intuition is a knowingness for me. I'm also aware of signals from the divine through numbers, animals and messages that come through in other ways too, such as the form of what people say, and song lyrics, for example.

Diane:

My intuition is very strong. If it says, "Turn left" and I don't, I am always on the wrong road. I listen to it daily to the best of my ability, and when I do, life works with ease and grace. When I think I know better (my ego), well, life isn't so simple. These days I just listen and do. I have strong intuition about people and places and it makes life much easier than second guessing myself.

Iris:

I generally just have this knowing.

I remember once I was seeing a patient, and I was stuck. I

literally took a step away and said out loud, "I need help" and I heard this sentence in my mind that contained the answer. That was pretty cool, and it remains the only time I have had verbal communication like that. When I am finishing up a treatment, I run my eyes across the patient's body and look for areas that might still be in distress. I don't see anything visually as such, but I do 'see' when they are there.

Practice
Tuning into your intuition

Consciously practice tuning into your intuitive feedback. You can use this to make the most conducive choices for almost anything.

Hold a question in your mind or compare two options. Tune in to notice:

- ∞ *Is my energy field brighter and bigger or smaller and darker?*
- ∞ *Does my body sway towards this option or away from it?*
- ∞ *Does this option make me stand up taller or make me slump?*
- ∞ *Does my body feel lighter or heavier?*

Practice this when you are choosing which food to buy, or if you are buying someone a present.

For example, when deciding where to go for a trip:

- ∞ *Does it light you up, or does it just feel like you will pay for it, with interest, energetically?*
- ∞ *Does one destination make you feel more expansive than another one?*

Once you are good at understanding your intuition, you will feel confident when you are choosing to buy a house to live in or a person to spend the rest of your life with.

Be aware that even though something feels right, it won't necessarily make it a walk in the well-manicured park. When I married for the first time, I felt on many levels that we were not a good match, but somehow it felt like it was what I should do in the bigger scheme of things. It was the beginning of the most difficult, challenging, gut-wrenching, heart-wrenching and shattering time of my life. But it also contained the seed of me finding out who I truly was and finding peace within myself.

Similarly, when my current husband and I decided to open our own business, we embarked on two years of exhaustion, challenges and difficulties, but on balance, eight years later, it was worth it. We both went through an extremely steep learning curve and some serious personal development.

Notice your spoken language, whether you say it out loud or not. What words do you use to describe anything? Sayings such as 'it makes me sick', 'pain in the neck (or rear)', 'it gives me the creeps', 'I am fed up' and so on, are true in your energy fields and quite likely in your body, too.

Guidance usually arrives in the energy field first. It's like a brush with a feather, gently showing you the way. If you ignore this guidance, it gets a bit stronger and starts showing up in your emotional field. You now have pebbles thrown at you, and it stings. You start feeling uncomfortable emotionally. If you persist in the direction you were going, you get bodily symptoms, such as nausea or fatigue. Now you have stones thrown at you, and the body feels discomfort. If you are really set in your ways and you still persevere, you get physically sick.

WHAT IS THE
INTENTION?

Everything has an energy, motivation or intention that is not always obvious on the surface. For example, a smile can be an expression of delight. Or a smile can be a way to cover up discomfort.

For instance, I made it a habit long ago to pick up rubbish when walking in nature. Sadly, sometimes the beauty of walking in nature got subsumed by picking up litter. I would get angry and annoyed and judgmental at humans who are so unaware that they leave their litter everywhere. Predictably, I would get home grumpy. The energy behind my picking up of rubbish was anger and annoyance.

I realised this didn't really help anyone, let alone raise the vibration of humanity. When I pick up rubbish now, I do it as an act of service. I think of the turtle, dolphin, bird, seahorse or fish that is not going to choke on this bit of plastic. My energy is one of care and consideration for my animal brothers and sisters. Picking up rubbish no longer subsumes my restorative walks, and I come home happy. Most of the time, anyway.

It never ceases to amaze me how systems and structures supposed to support humans quickly devolve into energetic black holes. An example might be unemployment benefits. If the benefit is given to a person with the energy of, "You are a loser, a deadbeat, a dropkick who cannot look after yourself and this payment is to make sure you don't end up in the gutter upsetting the more productive citizens," the outcome is different than if that same payment is given with the energy of, "You are a human being with inherent dignity fallen upon hard times. Here is some payment to ensure your basic needs are met so you can recover and start a new chapter in life."

If you spend time with mainstream media, check in with yourself. Does this bit of media empower, educate, and entertain you? Or does it make you feel fearful, disempowered or overwhelmed? Use your discernment to ensure you are giving your energy where it serves you.

It is fascinating how the same action can have completely different intentions behind it. For example, are you someone who chooses to eat fresh, organic food every day? Are you eating this food because you love the beautiful, nourishing, nurturing energy it gives your body? Or because it is important for you to know the Earth that produced this food has been honoured and the animal has been treated well? Or are you eating it because you are scared of getting cancer?

Choose your frequency

If in doubt, choose kindness.

Practice
Noticing and setting intentions

Imagine your day is a glass of pure, crystalline water, and you have the choice of what goes into that water.

Are you going to choose the gold dust of kindness, compassion, love, empathy and grace?

Or are you going to choose the mud of anger, envy, hatred and fear?

You will be the one drinking the water and spending the day.

Are your days predominantly gold dust or muddy days?

What is the intention you add to the glass of humanity every day?

FATIGUE

"There are two types of tired, I suppose.

One is a dire need of sleep.

The other is a dire need for peace."

—Mandeq Ahmed

What is your energy currency?

It is your attention.

Wherever your attention goes, your energy flows. Whatever you focus on, grows. You can focus on what sustains and nurtures you, or on what drains you.

It is not called 'paying' attention for no reason. When you pay attention, your focus and energy go towards whatever you are paying attention to. This is also called 'being present' with something or someone. When you fully pay attention to a person, listening to them to truly understand what they are saying, you feel their energy. When you fully pay attention to something, you can achieve a flow state where you are unaware of time slipping past, and you are just deeply immersed in the present moment.

I observe that most people try to get energy from other people. It's the half-full glass trying to fill itself up from another glass.

I was in a relationship once where we would have these 'discussions' or debates about fairly abstract things. He was a lawyer and quite a bit older than me. Most of the time he would 'win' and feel great! I would be utterly exhausted. He told me I was supposed to feel all buoyed too! And then, just once, I 'won' and I felt full of energy while he was all exhausted. That is a classic case of taking energy from one another, and the epitome of unsustainability.

Other ways people can take your energy include:

∞ Being late or keeping you waiting.
∞ Not responding, such as the silent treatment or ghosting.
∞ Having screaming matches with you.
∞ Lying to you.
∞ Gaslighting you.
∞ Having different rules for them and for you.
∞ Physical/emotional/financial/mental/spiritual abuse.
∞ Going back on their promises.
∞ Being unreliable.
∞ Expecting you to read their mind.
∞ Fishing for compliments.
∞ Making you wrong.
∞ Speaking over you.
∞ Incessant talking.
∞ Anything else that requires or forces you to pay attention to them.

So where can we get our energy from if not from each other?

"Now, every time I witness a strong person, I want to know: What dark did you conquer in your story? Mountains don't happen without earthquakes."

—Katherine MacKenett

Different kinds of fatigue and their remedies

Exhaustion comes in so many forms. Granted, they often travel together, and a lot of the remedies are the same. Most people don't know there are different types of exhaustion or how to recognise them. Instead of finding the best way to recover, they get overwhelmed and numb themselves instead.

Physical exhaustion

This kind of tiredness comes after physical activity, and not just from a massive sporting effort or from a heroic day in the garden. This kind of tiredness also arises if you concentrate on something outside yourself while in a sustained posture, like driving or sitting at a computer. Being in a sustained posture is not natural. It takes more effort to maintain than we realise. When our bodies are fatigued from the continuous effort and desperate for us to move, it often leads to pain.

Unwellness also puts us in need of physical rest. The body is either in fight-or-flight *or* in rest-and-digest. If you are unwell, or recovering from being unwell, and you re-join your stressful life before you are fully recovered, it takes a lot longer to get back to vitality because you are burning your depleted reserves.

My own example is when I had a relatively minor procedure done in hospital. The information sheet said it would only take a couple of days to feel better. It took me two weeks. At the time, I was an avid runner and had been running for an hour a day. But just the effort of getting in the car, driving for five minutes to the beach, sitting on the beach watching the dog dig holes—I didn't have the energy to actually walk him—and driving home utterly exhausted me.

Sources of physical energy

The answer is rest! Sleep is an obvious contender, and if you can bed down for a good night's sleep or a power nap, so much the better.

Sometimes you have had enough sleep and just need physical rest. This is a great time to watch your favourite series, read a book, chat with a friend, listen to music or do any other activity that occupies your mind pleasantly and allows your body to rest.

Daydreaming is important. When you do 'nothing', good ideas percolate in the background.

If you are well enough to move, but you still feel tired, sometimes a walk helps, particularly barefoot in nature. The Earth has an electromagnetic field, as do all creatures. By walking in bare feet, our electromagnetic field connects with Earth's field and can synchronise with it. Even just getting your feet on a patch of grass for a couple of minutes will help.

Other remedies for physical fatigue include a gentle yoga session, singing, dancing or meditating. All of these allow our brains to work in a more integrated way and help us to feel our bodies. Immersing the body in water, like a bath or shower or swimming are often restorative too.

Being truly present in your body and providing it with the rest it needs, rather than relying on your body to look after itself, allows your body to restore itself more deeply.

If you lack a particular nutrient, or nutrients, tiredness is often a consequence. You will know you are taking the right compound because it feels like the lights go back on!

And sometimes, all that's needed is a glass of water. When the body is thirsty and you drink water, you can feel your body re-energising.

"It takes courage to say yes to rest and play in a culture where exhaustion is seen as a status symbol."

—Brené Brown

Emotional exhaustion

This is when the emotions you have processed have been close to overwhelming. A fit of rage, a crying session or spending time feeling guilty or inadequate can all leave you emotionally exhausted.

If the emotions were overwhelming, you probably found yourself in numbness, which is a protective mechanism. It feels like utter disconnection from everything. You are unable to draw nurture from the beauty around you, such as a sunrise or a beautiful flower. You can't feel the love you have for people or even pets. This state of being is impervious to grief, sadness, disappointment and rejection, and, equally, unable to feel joy, light-heartedness, trust, connection and love. You can't feel *any* emotions. You are numb to them.

Sources of emotional energy

Sleep works for emotional fatigue, provided it isn't too much. Laughter is a great antidote. Even if it is forced to begin with, fake it till you make it. Find sources of light relief, read jokes, watch a funny movie, talk to a friend who is good at making you laugh. Have long, full-length body hugs, lasting 21 seconds or more from someone you love and trust. Play with your pet or the children in your life. Meditate. Immerse your body in nature or water. Music that makes your body move, sing or chant helps restore the energy. Do something creative that you know brings you joy.

Keep doing your chosen activity long enough, even if you feel resistance to start with, and the numbness will go. You will be able to process the intense emotions in smaller chunks at a time, and access the lighter emotions again, too.

Mental exhaustion

Have you ever spent a whole day, or a sleepless night, mulling over something?

Have you ever bought a car or renovated a house and been absolutely exhausted by the process? This is called decision-fatigue. It's likely you will sign the dotted line on a loan agreement you wouldn't have signed in a pink fit if it had been the first decision of the day. Our minds like to be busy, but sometimes they can also be exhausted and take off on their own tangent.

Sources of mental energy

Going for a walk, or doing other enjoyable physical movement helps. I love yoga to calm my mind when it is too busy. There's nothing quite like holding a balancing posture to get you back in the moment! Write it all down, so your subconscious knows you will not forget. Write in the dark if it's at night and keeping you awake. After two or three rounds of this, you will probably fall asleep. Occasionally, your scribblings could even be pretty good ideas in the light of day. Laugh. Meditate. Maybe do a meditation that requires visualisation, counting or using your hands. Our minds often chatter, even when we are doing something else. Tidy and clean your house. It's symbolic for clearing out the dross from your mind as well. Chant, dance or do any other activity that requires your full attention to be in and with your body.

"Rest is not idle, it is not wasteful. Sometimes rest is the most productive thing you can do for body and soul."

—Erica Layne

Spiritual fatigue

Spiritual fatigue is possibly the hardest kind to deal with. It's when the world and all that is wrong with it gets on top of you, and you don't know whether it's even worth going on because we are going to hell in a handbasket regardless of what you may or may not do. This is not true, but does appear to be real in many ways.

Today's young people are bombarded with doomsday messages more than previous generations ever were. You can't even enjoy a nature documentary without some message of despair. Catastrophes of all kinds are unfolding around us, begging us for attention and action. This leads to spiritual fatigue.

Sources of spiritual energy

The antidote to spiritual fatigue is to be truly present in the moment and feel deep gratitude for every little detail you can find right with the world, no matter how small or insignificant it might seem. This is far more important than we realise. Gratitude is a very high frequency that both your own body and being, as well as humanity, will benefit from. You are filling humanity's cup with gold dust and are helping to crowd out the mud in the process.

When my first marriage was in its death throes and I felt shattered on all levels, I drew joy from watching sparrows eat breadcrumbs.

Notice the beauty of a flower, a sunset, the stars sparkling in the night sky, the glittering of moonlight on water. Enjoy the breeze in your hair, the taste of your favourite food, the sound of your favourite music, the feeling of warm water on your body, the freedom of dance and singing. Connect with the loving gaze of someone you care about deeply, whether human or animal. Do an act of kindness, smile at a stranger, speak to the person at the checkout using their name, say "thank you" and mean it.

Sometimes, reminding yourself that human beings have survived harrowing conditions against all the odds and lived to flourish allows you to tap into your own strength, endurance and resilience in a whole new way. This is not to minimise what you are going through, but to get inspiration.

Think of Victor Frankl, for example, who was in a concentration camp in World War II, and survived with his capacity to feel compassion, forgiveness and love intact.

Anger can be a useful tool to get out of despair and hopelessness. These emotions are low energy states, whereas anger has energy that can give you the push you need to carry on until you find joy in your life again.

Know that it is not only ok, but required, for you to rest and take time out, to do what fills you up. The cliché that you cannot draw water from an empty well applies to you too.

Have faith that you are enough.

Truly pay attention to the small, joyful, miraculous moments happening to all of us, many times a day. Appreciate the beauty and the love offered to you daily, in whatever form it comes. Find your tribe, draw on your community.

Turn to your own guidance. Trust that even though life looks bleak right now, your record of getting through hard times so far is 100% and that you will get through this too. You don't have to know how to get through this whole period. You only need to know how to get through this day, or even just this moment.

Know that beautiful, loving, creative, kind and compassionate humans are doing good deeds all the time, even though it doesn't make the news all that often.

Trust that the Universe knows what it's doing. Even if you

don't understand right now, you will down the track, and you will be glad you hung in there.

Remind yourself that you are only in charge of *your* piece of the mosaic, or puzzle, and that from your vantage point you cannot see the whole artwork you are a part of. Saving the world is a communal effort, and this effort is going on even if you can't perceive it right now. Showing up every day and doing your best, shining your light and choosing kindness makes a bigger difference than you might think.

Whatever lights you up is what you came here to do, so do it! Your unique quirk or interest or enthusiasm or hobby is needed and serves a purpose. It can be as diverse as raising a child or inventing a machine that cleans up our air. Trust that if you don't know the first thing about inventing machines, someone else does, and it might just be the child you are raising! Chunk it down to small acts that aren't overwhelming. Do what you can without burning yourself out.

Trust that the Universe knows what it is doing and has it all in hand.

"The whole world is a series of miracles, but we are so used to them we call them ordinary things."

—Hans Christian Andersen

Interviews with women about fatigue

What makes you feel fatigued?
And what are your strategies to deal with it?

Megan:
When I am not aligned.
When my boundaries are not strong.
When I say yes and mean no or vice versa.
When I have a fibromyalgia attack!

Beckie:
Lack of sleep, lack of water, processed foods, and stress cause me to feel fatigued. Since becoming a mum, lack of sleep and broken sleep hasn't affected me as much as it did before.

Prue:

I would say emotional and energetic fatigue hits me stronger than physical fatigue. If I'm veering off path, doubting myself, stuck in an unhelpful thought-loop or surrounded by deflated people, these all leave me feeling fatigued.

My strategies to feel energised include nature, walking on the beach with my pup, connecting with other soul-centred people, being creative, singing, writing, drawing, crafting, eating delicious and wholesome food, listening to fabulous music and laughing. I laugh a lot!

Diane:

Fatigue is, according to the dictionary, a daily lack of energy which I rarely feel. Tiredness, on the other hand, is simply when I have done too much, be it the computer, the garden, whatever. Fatigue is not a familiar feeling to me at all. When I am tired, I just learned, in my seventies, that my body is saying, "Woah, slow down, Goddess." So I go lay on the couch and pick up a book, or sit in the sun and contemplate the ocean. I am soooo much better at taking care of myself these days and I think it comes with age. I have been blessed with an overabundance of energy for my whole life. I can run a seminar for two and a half days or five days and be high as a kite at the end, whereas the participants can be exhausted.

Iris:

I feel fatigue when I don't listen to my body about rest or water or food. I am still learning how to pace myself!

I feel fatigue when I feel into all the unnecessary and thoughtless—and at times gleeful—destruction of living beings and the planet. I just know there is a better way for humanity to interact with our beautiful, awe-inspiring and only home in space.

This is a tricky one to deal with. I remind myself that it isn't up to me to make everything right. Many others are holding the light as well. I am only responsible for what I can do, and I too need rest and joy. Then I get back to doing what I can do.

"How cool is it that the Divine force who created mountains, oceans, and galaxies, looked at you and thought the world needs one of you, too."

—Unknown

Strategies to fuel your life

Spend time in nature

This remedies physical, emotional, mental and spiritual fatigue. The trick is, as always, to truly pay attention to the present moment, to where you are and what you are experiencing. It is possible to go for a walk along the beach, mull over that persistent thought and not take in any of the beauty of the walk. This happens to all of us. But at least your body will feel refreshed and nourished.

Walk on the Earth with bare feet

Our Earth has an electromagnetic field, just like our bodies do. By putting your bare feet on the ground, your body attunes itself to Earth's field. This is a brilliant strategy if you have been travelling by car or by plane, where you lose touch with Earth's electromagnetic field. It's great if you are feeling ungrounded for any reason or you need to physically recharge. Pay attention to the soles of your feet connecting with the different textures and energies present.

Sleep

Sleep is helpful for all kinds of fatigue. Before the advent of electric lights and screens, humans used to sleep for nine hours a night, as well as nap during the day. In our times, it is not unusual for people to make do with six hours of sleep a night and be busily productive all day. This is not conducive to thriving. When we sleep at night, the brain releases a hormone called melatonin which repairs the brain. Inadequate sleep is a quick way to ensure our bodies and our brains break down faster.

Too much sleep can be an issue as well. Have you experienced a time when you woke up, having slept enough, but then went back to sleep and woke up feeling groggy and flat? Sleep can be a way to escape reality. Rather than sleep too much, try movement to make you feel good.

Breath

Oxygen is the single most important nutrient for our bodies. Most of us breathe shallowly all day, which is not conducive to proper oxygen and carbon dioxide ratios in our blood. It can make us feel anxious. Taking deep, slow, conscious breaths into the bottom of our ribcage not only helps to oxygenate our blood optimally, it also stimulates the parasympathetic (rest, digest, relax, feel safe, heal) parts of our nervous system. This is beneficial for all types of fatigue. Many different kinds of meditation are based on conscious breathing.

Water

Water is the second most important nutrient for the body after oxygen. If you feel flat, have some water. If you feel hungry, have some water. If you are still hungry half an hour later, eat something. Many people mistake thirst for hunger. If you feel emotional, have some water. If you sit for too long, get up and have some water. If you have physical symptoms, have some water.

Our bodies are roughly two-thirds water. If we deplete our internal water stores even a little, the body quickly develops subtle symptoms which become more obvious the longer it goes on.

If you are thirsty, drinking water feels like fuel and the water tastes sweet, provided you have good quality water. Say a blessing over the water or feel gratitude for the water while you drink it.

It is possible to overdose on water. It does, however, take a lot of perseverance to drink too much water, usually over several days, to achieve this. When your body is happily hydrated, water tastes insipid, which is the signal from your body that it has had enough for now.

Immersion in water

Water is amazingly restorative, on all levels, when the body is immersed in it, be it a shower, a bath, a lake, a river or the sea.

Food

Food should be a source of energy. If you feel flat after eating, what you are consuming is not compatible with your body. Choose foods that are as nature created them, with the least amount of packaging and processing.

Eat when you are hungry. Stop and tune into what kind of food your body would like for nourishment. Cooked foods? Raw foods? Fruit? Nuts and seeds? Chocolate? If you always have easy access to food, allow your body to feel hungry for a little while. This increases your intuitive sense of what kind of food your body is asking for.

Eat slowly. Concentrate on your food. Stop eating when you are no longer hungry, rather than when you feel full or even bloated. Studies show that people and animals who eat to 80% satiety live longer.

If you are eating for emotional reasons, be aware that this is the case. If you need chocolate, or whatever your comfort food is, to soothe your emotions, make it a conscious experience. If you do, you will likely feel better after just one piece, whereas if you berate yourself and feel guilty for eating the chocolate, you are likely to eat the whole bar without even noticing. Sometimes, you just need to do what you need to do to get yourself through the day or night. It is a part of the human experience and just requires acceptance.

Practice
Eating your favourite 'naughty' food

Have your piece of chocolate, or whatever your food is, and do nothing else while you eat it.
Close your eyes.
Feel the texture in your mouth.
Savour the flavour.
Make the experience last in your mouth.
How do you feel after eating just one morsel of your 'naughty' food this way?

"The cure for anything is salt water: sweat, tears or the sea."

—Karen Blixen

Affection

Our bodies need affection to thrive. It is one of the best antidotes to stress. Ideally, exchange full body hugs with someone you care about and feel safe with for 21 seconds or longer. It lowers stress and improves your immunity.

If you are not exchanging affection with another human, give affection to an animal. Hopefully you have been chosen by an animal to be their companion. If you don't have a cuddly pet, give your body affection in the way of baths, massages (ideally by someone else), facial treatments, mani- or pedicures, reflexology, or choose your own favourite. Give your body words of appreciation if everything else is unavailable to you.

Sunshine

Sunshine feels good for a reason! I have an intuitive knowing that our bodies consume light as a fuel. Sunshine also has many biochemical effects on the body. It affects mood, regulates the daily, monthly and yearly rhythms of the body, and is essential for Vitamin D, the 'sunshine vitamin', production in our skin. Anyone who has lived in darkness-filled parts of the world, due to the sun not clearing the horizon or continuously overcast skies, knows the uplifting effect of sunlight and blue skies and seeks it out whenever it is available.

It goes without saying that sunburn is too much of a good thing.

Meditation

Meditation is a wonderful tool for recovering from physical, emotional, mental and spiritual fatigue. At times, trying to meditate can be frustrating because our minds race around trying to find something to do. Or you go to the empty space within and your mind comments, "Oh, I am doing it!" completely breaking the spell. Personally, I find it useful to keep my mind occupied by allowing it to follow a guided meditation or by doing a yogic type breathing meditation, for example, alternate nostril breathing.

Check out my YouTube channel https://www.youtube.com/@ irisangellys if you'd like a meditation playlist for inspiration.

Resting and daydreaming

Sometimes, our bodies are tired, but our minds, emotions or spirits are not. For those days, just resting, having a cup of tea while watching the day go by, bingeing on movies, or doing something creative can be greatly restorative to our bodies. Daydreaming is essential for human wellbeing!

In our Western culture, productivity has become the be-all-and-end-all. But if you think about it, who invents new things, creates amazing works of art, or cooks the most amazing meals? People who have leisure! Leisure is the luxury of having significant chunks of time without anything scheduled into them, to do with as you please. Not so long ago, people who had leisure were landowners and aristocrats. No wonder they felt others should derive a sense of self from working harder!

Many of us dread long stretches of leisure because those are the spaces when we are often invited to process old issues we put away for 'later'. But, if you can get to the space within yourself where you enjoy your own company, leisure is going to be a time where you recharge, either by yourself or with people you care about. Leisure allows you to be at your most creative. This is where the juice of living is to be found.

"We're not saying you should take 42 percent of your time to rest; we're saying if you don't take the 42 percent, the 42 percent will take you. It will grab you by the face, shove you to the ground, put its foot on your chest, and declare itself the victor."

—Emily Nagoski, ***Burnout: The Secret to Unlocking the Stress Cycle***

Spending time

Most of us frequently say, "I don't have time!", then spend four hours watching TV or computer or phone screens that same day. These devices are the ultimate time, energy and attention thieves. No prizes for guessing why you don't have time or energy!

The funny thing about time is you can only *spend* it. We talk about saving time, but this is not possible. We can only spend it on something else. It is striking that we live in such a wealthy culture, with any number of machines doing the work we used to do by hand, and yet we have less time than ever for each other or for joyful activities.

If you are truly present in your body, you spend your time consciously, choosing with awareness what you want to use your precious and irretrievable time on. When you allow yourself to be present, you feel like you have more time. Remember endless summer days as a child? You know how to do this. You will feel full and satisfied at the end of the day rather than drained.

Music

Music is another fantastic tool for emotional, mental and spiritual fatigue. Music can help us process every, any and all states of mind and heart. Music can uplift us or calm us down.

Music involves using the whole brain in a way that doesn't happen otherwise. If you play an instrument, it is even more powerful, because your brain is activated by your body's fine movements. If you use your voice as your instrument, it is even more potent.

If you don't like singing, chant. You can chant anything, but the yogic mantra AUM is the most well-known. I love chanting because you can process energy stuck in your body without having to know what it was all about. After just five minutes of chanting, your whole body feels tingly and alive. Try it! This is not just for Tibetan monks.

Movement

Movement is essential for wellbeing. 90% of the information to the brain from the body comes from our joints, ligaments, bones and muscles. Brain cells need three things to function well: oxygen, nutrients and stimulation. Most stimulation of our brain cells starts with input from moving our bodies. This is why we feel stiff and flat after a day of sitting.

It doesn't matter what sort of movement you engage in, as long as you enjoy it. Walking is a good start, but any movement that makes you feel like you have used your body in a purposeful and satisfying way is great.

Creativity

Creativity is a fuel. It doesn't matter if it is dancing, basket-weaving, gardening, knitting, painting, singing, playing an instrument, sewing, writing or whatever your favourite thing is. Creativity helps us to get into a flow state, where we are so immersed in what we are doing that we lose track of time. This is a way to connect with the Greater All. Engage with whatever gives you joy, whether you are good at it or not. What matters is that it feeds your soul. It will give you strength and stamina for whatever else you might need to do or deal with. I was lucky enough to visit Samoa a number of years ago. The ladies who cleaned the rooms would sing in three-part harmony. We spent time outside our room just listening to it. I am sure their work would have been so much easier and enjoyable with the singing.

On a different note, I recently learnt that many new mums don't sing to their babies anymore, feeling that they aren't good singers. That is completely beside the point! It is about you nurturing your child, and your child feeling your body's vibrations and getting to know you, not about some perfectly edited production. This goes for dads too.

"If you feel something calling you to dance or write or paint or sing, please refuse to worry about whether you are good enough. Just do it."

—Glennon Doyle

Dancing

Dancing combines movement, music and connection (depending on whether you are dancing on your own or not). Humans have been making music with their voices and instruments, and dancing since the dawn of humanity. Dancing is one of the best ways to move energy in your body and express whatever is present for you at the time.

Dance like no-one is watching. Do it for you!

Body treatments

It is surprising just how much better you feel after an encounter with a bodywork healer. Think chiropractic, massage, reflexology, kinesiology, acupuncture, etc. When you are physically, emotionally, mentally or spiritually drained, a skilled practitioner often switches the lights back on for you, allowing your body to either rest to restore itself or feel energised and alive again.

Communication

Talking to a friend is a balm for many hurt feelings, minds and spirits. Explaining a situation out loud often allows us to observe a situation from a different perspective and move through whatever it is. Sometimes, just someone truly listening to you to understand you, rather than thinking about their reply, is enough for us to have a breakthrough. To be seen, heard, respected and understood is healing.

Someone we trust can often give a different perspective on a situation. They see the issue from the outside and can help us approach it differently. Writing your thoughts down can be therapeutic too, depending on how you like to process.

Some people talk about the same thing over and over again, without endeavouring to find an actual solution or outcome. This is another way of staying stuck and draining your energy. If you are with such a person, ask them what they plan to do about it. You often get a blank look, like it has never occurred to them that they might change things. You may have to stop engaging with that person on that topic if all they do is drain you while they stay stuck.

Community

Community creates immunity. Humans are social creatures and we have a deep need to feel like we are among people who like us and are like us, who understand us and who have our welfare at heart. People with a deep sense of community live longer. We all need a space where we can let our guard down. But be aware how much of yourself you give in any community you are in. Sometimes, we compromise our core to fit in which means this is not truly your tribe. In the long run, this will not serve you.

Stories

Children love stories for a reason. Humans have told each other stories since the beginning of humanity. Stories entertain and stories teach. Stories let us live entire lifetimes in our imagination. Stories create new worlds to explore. Stories create culture and cement values. Stories allow us to explore different ways of being in the world and let us understand their consequences without having to try it out in real life. Stories in books or on a screen can be fabulous ways to allow the body to rest while refreshing the mind, emotions and spirit.

Joy

While I was growing up, I absorbed a strong work ethic. It was desirable to always be productive. It was fine to have fun while being productive, but it was important to have been useful before frivolously having fun just for the sake of it. Homework was done before going to play.

I grew up to be a diligent, trustworthy and productive citizen.

The problem with making sure you do your homework before you go to play as an adult is the homework never ends, especially when you are doing a tertiary degree, performing a full-time job and/or have a family with children or elders who need looking after. By the time you get around to finishing your day's work and chores, there is often no longer the time and energy to do anything purely for pleasure. The next day, the whole cycle starts again. It's a bit of an alarm bell when even the activities you choose to do for pleasure end up being chores, such as practicing guitar or walking the dog. Exhaustion, resentment and lack of joy become normal.

The irony is that when your tanks are full, and you have done something purely to feel alive, engaged, curious and revived, all those other matters become a non-issue. They happen easily, with a spring in your step. I am sure you are familiar with, "I'll just quickly do this...", then the computer plays up, or the printer jams, or you can't find something hiding in plain sight. The 'quick' activity takes two or three times longer and five times the energy it reasonably should.

Whom do we serve by using joy as a reward rather than a fuel? Absolutely no one! Your spouse likely prefers you to be happy rather than having a neat, tidy house and gourmet meals.

Ironically, it takes discipline to begin with. If you need to, set an alarm to make sure you stop when you intend to. Life has sweetness again once you fuel it with joy like you did as a child.

Gratitude

In our society, we have been conditioned to focus on what is not right or not enough or not 'good'. What we focus on grows, and this tends to lead to a life that feels lacking. Gratitude is the antidote to this. We have so much to be grateful for! If you don't live in a war zone and have a healthy body, regular food, shelter, running water in your house, and someone who cares about you, everything else is a problem of affluence. We truly have so much to be grateful for. Spend time every day focusing on what is right and beautiful in your world. Hug your loved ones a little longer.

Counting your blessings is the antidote to the draining feeling of lack.

Practice
Gratitude Diary

Keep a gratitude diary. Every day, write three things down that you are grateful for. Start by writing "I am grateful for ...." At every sentence. This might seem onerous, but it engages your body in a whole new way with the energy of gratitude. Make it a practice ideally for a year, but at least for 3 months, and you will be amazed at how your life changes.

"Piglet noticed that even though he had a Very Small Heart, it could hold a very large amount of Gratitude."

—A. A. Milne, Winnie-the-Pooh

Beauty

Beauty of nature, humans, and human creation uplifts the mind, spirit and emotions. Connect with a sunrise or sunset, a body of water, a plain or a mountain range. Connect with the majesty of a forest of tall trees or a cathedral. Connect with art or the beauty of the eyes and the smile of another being.

Curiosity

Curiosity may have killed the cat, but it keeps humans alive. Adults generally take life far too seriously. If we have decided that "this is how things are supposed to be!", and someone comes along who has a completely different take on life, it can feel challenging or frightening, which are draining states to be in.

How about we approach anything or anyone new or different with an attitude of, "I wonder what that feels like? I wonder what that means?" Allow the other person to tell you what their experience is with an open mind, and without a preconceived notion of what you think it should be. Try to imagine experiencing what they are telling you. It may not be something that suits you or your circumstances, but at least you have had an unexpected vicarious adventure.

The moment we stop being curious, the moment we stop growing as human beings, is the moment we start dying inside.

"Travelling through life with curiosity rather than judgement is how one finds the magic in each moment."

—Erin Chatters

Gratitude is

Gratitude is a soft breeze on your skin
And sun on your face
And laughter with friends

Gratitude is a loving caress
And making beautiful food to share

Gratitude is cold clean water to drink
Hot water in the shower
And a splash in a river or lake or ocean

Gratitude is
Watching animals at play
And hearing children laugh

Gratitude is
A shelter
Food on the table
Someone who cares for me

Gratitude is
Breath
Heartbeat
Connection to Earth
Connection to Source

Gratitude is
The stars in the night sky
The moon and the sun
Especially at dusk and at dawn
Gratitude is
Birdsong
Dancing
Friendship
And belonging

Gratitude is
Being curious about new things
Exploring
And inspiration

Gratitude is
Seeing colours
Smelling scents
Tasting food
And petting soft skin or fur or feathers

Gratitude is
The gift
Of being alive

EVERYTHING
IS ENERGY

$e=mc^2$

I am sure everyone has come across this equation. Rearranged, it shows that mass is energy that has slowed down a lot, by roughly 90,000,000,000 km/s. It also means that if you speed up mass, or matter, by that same factor, it becomes energy.

For instance, ice is slow water, which in turn is slow water vapour. It's all H_2o, just at different speeds.

Everything is energy. Some of it feels solid, and some of it feels like sensations in our bodies or looks like light, but it's all energy. Our bodies are energy made out of atoms that consist of little units of energy and space. Our emotions are energy. Our thoughts are energy. Our spirits are energy. These are different kinds of energy that vibrate at different speeds. This is how they can all coexist in the same space.

Suddenly the world looks a lot less solid, right?

Think of it like this: you have a cup of tea in front of you, and you add honey to it. The honey dissolves. While there isn't noticeably more fluid in the cup, the flavour is quite different.

What's so good about knowing this is that your emotions, thoughts, behaviours and habits are also energy, meaning you can deal with them as energy. You can observe them, notice their qualities, and not take them personally.

I like to visualise it like this: think of the night sky, studded with stars, brilliant, mysterious, vast and awe-inspiring. This is your being. A thought, emotion, belief or behaviour comes across your field like a cloud. You watch the cloud pass, knowing that the night sky is still there in all its glory.

Sometimes, they are big, thick clouds with rain, snow, hail, or thunder and lightning. You can still watch them pass, knowing the night sky is only temporarily obscured by the storm.

Some clouds, such as thoughts, beliefs, behaviours and emotions, come across our sky that we don't like. We judge them, don't accept them or don't enjoy them, and most of us immediately start resisting them. That's like putting a lightning rod right next to you and holding on tightly, so all the weather is attracted to you and any lightning hits you with the biggest possible force.

A different analogy is this: you are floating along a river on an inflatable li-lo. Some of the time, the going is slow and meandering, sometimes there are rapids. You manage to steer your way through the rapids, but every so often you bump up against a rock, such as an undesirable thought, emotion, behaviour or belief. At this point, you can cling on to the rock, telling the rock it is in the wrong place, has hurt you, is stopping your pleasant ride down the river and is making your life miserable. Or you can push off and keep going, having learnt how to bump into rocks and become wiser about avoiding them in the future.

If you can understand the essential energetic nature of everything, if you can understand that emotions (anger, sadness, guilt, elation), thoughts (I am not good enough, I will never succeed), beliefs (which are essentially habitual thoughts and emotions) and behaviours (sulking, smoking), are at their essence just energy, you will realise you are not stuck with them. All you need to do is observe them, acknowledge them, take the information they provide you and allow them to leave your energy field.

Come on an imaginary journey with me

Imagine you are born into a tribe where the colour yellow is the epitome of everything bad and undesirable. This tribe believes that if you ever see yellow, you will die instantly. There is no yellow in your home, and you are not allowed to eat yellow foods. If you are an artist, there is no yellow on the palette. Green and orange are frowned upon in purist circles too, because they are closely related to yellow. You are not allowed to wear gold jewellery because gold is shiny yellow. If you are a musician, you aren't allowed to compose or play the note C because it is the musical equivalent of yellow. The number 8 is similarly fraught, but more difficult to avoid because counting is inaccurate without it. Anytime you are outside, you need to wear blue, purple or red glasses to ensure you don't see yellow. People with colour blindness are sent to live away from your tribe because they could inadvertently introduce yellow to the tribe. But that's ok, because they are exalted, having been saved from ever seeing yellow.

One day, you are walking along the street, and an insect flies beneath your coloured glasses and makes your eye water and sting. You need to take the glasses off and attend to this, because your eye is hurting, even although it potentially puts you in harm's way. When you have dealt with the insect and you look up, you see the most stunning golden and yellow sunset. You are speechless, in awe of the beauty.

Nothing else happens.

You put the glasses on and go home, puzzled by this occurrence. You try not to appear changed, even though on the inside you are no longer the same person. You broke the rules! You didn't mean to, but these finer points are not up for discussion. More to the point, nothing bad happened as a consequence. Your eyes hurt a bit to start with, having not seen this shade before, but you didn't die.

One day, you accidentally hear music composed by someone who uses the note C, and you hear amazing harmonies you never heard before, soothing and uplifting your heart. You notice this music sounds different from what you are used to, but don't realise till later why this was the case.

You start questioning whether what your tribe takes as set in stone is true?

One day, quite by accident, you eat mango. It is a completely new fruit to you, and you don't know it is yellow because you are still wearing your coloured glasses. The heavenly sweetness explodes in your mouth, beauty on a spoon. Then you realise this is a forbidden yellow fruit. But instead of harming you, it makes your body feel amazing!

At this point, you decide this whole idea of condemning one colour is utter nonsense. You decide to leave your tribe and live with all your senses aware and awake to every colour, sound, smell and experience life has to offer. You smell daffodils. You admire sunrises and sunsets. Your eyes hurt when you found out you shouldn't look directly at the sun. You listen to all kinds of music. You find out that you don't like pineapple much.

You realise how much Life you were missing out on before, when you followed the rules of Yellow.

Imagine how much more energy is now available to you. All the energy, effort, alertness and diligence that went into avoiding and resisting the experience of yellow, you can now use for all sorts of other activities!

What is your yellow?

You might well be thinking that trying to exclude a colour from your life is rather absurd. But if you substitute yellow with any emotion in the human spectrum of experience, it becomes equally absurd to want to exclude any of them from your options of experience.

If you can stop judging what you are experiencing as good or bad, right or wrong, mine or not mine, us and them, all you have left is experience. If you can approach everything as energy, just observing, you free up the energy that went into resisting these experiences until now. You don't have massive encounters with these unpleasant energies because you are no longer amplifying the experience by resisting it.

What you resist, persists.

What you focus on, grows.

Some of these experiences are pleasant and wonderful. Some of them feel unpleasant.

The positive aspect of unpleasant experiences is that they unlock more potential inside you, often potential you didn't know you had. With this attitude, you can welcome everything Life offers you as something to celebrate or something to learn from. Even if it feels unpleasant at the time.

When you come across something that feels alien to you, feel into it and use your discernment, rather than judgement. Allow your heart to guide you about whether you are wise to pursue this experience or not.

This mindset equally allows us to see our fellow humans as beings who are expressing and experiencing other aspects of human potential. We can allow them to explore whatever they want to without judging them.

When you encounter something new and unknown, approach it with curiosity, and it becomes interesting rather than threatening.

Try it!

"I am not the calm before the storm. I am both the calm and the storm."

—Ivy Atalanta

Emotions, thoughts, behaviours, habits, beliefs

How can you relate to your emotions, thoughts, behaviours and beliefs as energy rather than unpleasantness the Universe is punishing you with?

What are they, and do they serve a purpose?

Emotions are feedback. They let you know where you are at with anything at any given time.

Thoughts are interpretations we assign to any given situation so we can understand it better.

Beliefs are thoughts we have accepted as truth. We filter our perceptions through them.

Behaviours are the actions we take based on our emotions, thoughts and beliefs.

Habits are emotions, thoughts and behaviours we have repeated so frequently that we now do them automatically, without even noticing anymore.

Keep in mind that emotions, thoughts, behaviours and habits can be, and often are, based on incomplete or downright faulty information. Also keep in mind that most of the time, they arise together, but for the sake of clarity we will examine them individually.

I use these strategies and they work for me. However, if you are in deep distress, I urge you to seek out a professional who can hold space for you.

Emotions

Our true nature as human beings is love. We need to understand that there is a difference between our core frequency, love, and the fleeting emotions that show up in our lives.

If we continuously seek something in the world outside ourselves to make us happy, we will be on a perpetual wild goose chase, trying to get to the next fad that will make us feel good, and frequently bumping into all sorts of other distractions that make us feel bad.

If we can live in the awareness of our own signature frequency, such as love, gratitude, joy, kindness and serenity, we can allow and accept all emotions knowing they are merely feedback. We can stop depending on good emotions to feel good. Resting in our hearts, in our true nature, stops us from being victims of circumstances and lets us feel a deep sense of wellbeing, regardless of what is going on for us. We know that life happens *for* us, not *to* us.

For example, imagine you are working hard at your company with an eye for promotion. You have this mindset that once you get this promotion, you will be happy because you will have extra status, a new business card with gold lettering on it and more money. You get promoted. You feel happy and excited and flush with success. You worked hard to earn this promotion!

Will this promotion give you long-term happiness? If you are not living from awareness of your own true nature, it will be very temporary indeed, and you will be back on the hamster wheel, looking for the next boost. If, on the other hand, you are living with awareness of your own true nature, you will not depend on the promotion to feel happy. You might even turn it down, because you are aware it will require more time and energy from you than you are prepared to give.

The first step, when an emotion comes up, is simply to notice it. We often get swept away by emotions. In the process, we forget the emotions are not who we are. It's important to know we are larger than our emotions. We contain them, not the other way around. We are the night sky, not the clouds.

Second, observe the emotion. Feel it. Where can you feel it? Is it in your body or your energy field? What does it feel like? How intense is it? Does it have a colour or a texture? Is it pleasant or unpleasant? Are any memories or images associated with it? Are any behaviours associated with it? Is a story attached to it? Does this story feel true to all of you or just to a part of you?

Third, don't resist it. What you resist, persists. Allow it to be present and move through your body and energy field. Watch the cloud move across your field of vision. It will be gone in the space of minutes at most. If you want to give it a helping hand, take some deep, conscious breaths, and visualise yourself breathing it out.

Remember that emotion is just feedback about what is going on for you. It is an energy passing through your energy field like a cloud passing over your night sky. There is no need to think it's a bad cloud, or permanent, or that this cloud can diminish the night sky, even if it is big, heavy and fluffy.

Many people try to think their way out of emotions. They justify or create a story to avoid feeling what they are feeling. The only way thoughts can be helpful is if new information comes to light that changes your perception and understanding of what is going on.

The other trap with emotions is wanting to hold on to the pleasant ones, such as the euphoria of falling in love. But no emotion is ever permanent. Emotions are feedback. What is being asked of us is to accept ourselves as the whole beings we are and to accept we are a vessel that Life moves through. Allow the desirable emotions to move through you just as much as you allow the unpleasant ones to move through you.

We can get addicted to any emotion, even the ones we don't like feeling. Every emotion has a biochemical molecule that signals to the cells in the body that we are currently experiencing it. As we get older and we find our way of being in the world, we also find our basic emotional tone. This could be a predominant emotion of irritability, depression, optimism, fear, guilt, happiness or any other feeling you care to name.

The more you experience a type of emotion, the more receptors the body's cells make for that emotion. This means the predominant emotion in your life has the biggest number of receptors on the cells' surfaces. These receptors need a hit of their molecule on a regular basis. If they are deprived of their molecules of emotion long enough, you will get cravings and find a reason in the outside world to feel this emotion again.

For example, a young woman who is habitually melancholy gets a proposal of marriage. She is happy and excited, plans for her big day and has a wonderful time at her wedding. Soon after the nuptials, she returns to her depressed state. She might even have a rebound and get extra depressed once she comes off the high the wedding gave her. This is someone who can find a cloud for every silver lining.

Most of us probably know a grumpy old man. Even if you have fantastic news to share, the conversation always reverts to what's wrong with the world.

Someone whose basic setting is optimism finds the gem in every stone. When they go through trying times, they find a valuable lesson they put into their resilience toolbox for future use.

This is why both optimists and pessimists are always right. This is why two people in similar circumstances finds one of them seeing defeat, while the other sees opportunity.

This addiction to a particular emotion is no different from any other addiction to a chemical, such as nicotine in tobacco. In fact, the reason these addictive substances work in the first place is because they interact with a particular kind of receptor.

The good news is there are ways to speed up processing emotions. You can choose to proactively process emotions in a more dynamic way. It's about getting creatively expressive. Here are some ideas – use the ones that are easiest for you to start with.

Singing. Find the music that feels most appropriate and sing your heart out. It doesn't have to sound pretty.

Toning is chanting or humming. Ideally it should be a vowel sound. "Aum" is probably the most well-known sound, but it can be any sound that feels right to you. If something feels stuck in a part of the body, or an area of your life, you can direct the sound to that area and use it to move that energy on. The vibration of sound travels through your body. Even if you only do this for a couple of minutes, you feel the difference in your energy field afterwards. It makes you feel tingly and vibrant. The beauty of this practice is you don't even need to know what the energy was all about to process it.

Allow your body to cry if it needs to. Tears are raindrops of the soul. Different types of tears have different chemical compositions. They cleanse the emotion from your body.

Dancing is another great way to process emotions. Just move your body however it wants to be moved. It doesn't have to look good. It just has to *feel* good. Just move to whatever music moves you at that moment.

Crafting can be therapeutic too. Splash paint where it feels right or use clay to sculpt a creation.

Write it all down and burn it symbolically when you are done to symbolise you have finished with it.

Anything that allows you to give the emotion a manifestation outside yourself can be useful.

The key with these approaches or practices is to create without an outcome in mind, and not to judge what happens.

You might find a story emerges in your sound, movement or colourful expression. This is your subconscious telling you what is going on. It's great if that happens, but it doesn't matter if it doesn't. Sometimes we are better off not knowing or we don't need to clutter our minds with it. Trust that you will know what you need to know when you need to know it. Have fun exploring!

"In Irish when you talk about an emotion, you don't say, 'I am sad.' You'd say, 'Sadness is on me – Ta' Bron Orm.' I love that because there's an implication of not identifying yourself with the emotion fully. I am not sad, it's just that sadness is on me for a while. Something else will be on me another time, and that's a good thing to recognize."

—Padraig O. Tuama

Thoughts

Thoughts are our interpretations of what is going on within and around us. Most of us think in words. Most of us have this little internal voice authoritatively interpreting what is going on. But there is no internal logic to it. One moment it can proclaim blue is green as a definite truth. And the next, it can proclaim that blue is yellow with just as much conviction. Occasionally, it might even say blue is blue.

The problem is most of us aren't aware this dialogue is happening. This voice jabbers along in the background, commenting incessantly, and most of us tune out. We can't quite remember what this voice said previously because we don't pay conscious attention to it, so we don't notice the contradictions.

It colours how we feel because these interpretations evoke emotional responses in many instances. And we wonder why we are suddenly feeling so bad!

Have you ever come across someone who talks incessantly? Who verbalises every thought that pops into their head without filtering or summarising any of it? That is what goes on in our heads for most of us, most of our waking hours. How is it possible to continuously engage with that? No wonder we tune out!

Thoughts can be just as seductive as emotions, and we can get our energy wrapped up and stuck in them. Anyone who has ever had a sleepless night mulling over an obsessive thought knows what I am talking about.

The first thing with thoughts is to notice you are having them. Pay conscious attention to that little voice. You might even challenge what it says and see what happens. As you observe this commentary, hold the knowledge that what is said may or may not be true. This is a crucial point. Do I know this is true? Am I sure this is true? Could it possibly be untrue, or not the whole truth? And watch the little voice pause for breath!

When I have an obsessive thought, I have a lot of emotion wrapped up in my current interpretation of the world. Most of the time, I am missing at least one crucial bit of information. Once I get this bit of information, my perception of the issue can change in an instant.

If just paying attention to the dialogue is not breaking the chatter, it can be useful to give it a life outside your head by writing it down or recording it. Your mind no longer needs to keep track of the thoughts and can start to relax. Sometimes you have to go through that process a few times for the mind to feel complete. Occasionally, valuable insights are contained in what you have recorded. You will know by the feeling in your body.

Speaking the thoughts out loud to a friend gives you the opportunity to hear a different perspective. Tell them it's OK for them to interrupt you when they have a curveball to throw you. They can take on the role of observer in this instance, which is useful if you have a difficult train of thought to shift.

Find those missing pieces of information. Ask others how they would approach the situation you feel stuck in, particularly people you feel deal with that kind of situation well. The trick is often to do something different than normal. Reclaim your power of choice. Once you have changed something, even just a tiny something, you can gain more insight and change something else.

Another fun way to observe your thoughts is to change the voice that speaks it. Is it your own voice? A parent's? A teacher's? Try changing the voice to Donald Duck's and notice if it still feels true and so serious!

"That was the thing about thoughts. They thought themselves, and then dropped into your head in the hope that you would think so too."

—Terry Pratchett , *"I Shall Wear Midnight"*

Behaviours

Behaviours are how we move in the world in response to how we feel and think. If you engage in a behaviour that has an unhelpful impact on your life, find out what unacknowledged thoughts and emotions are driving it and process them.

To find out whether your behaviours are helping you to navigate life, observe whether your behaviours align with what you consciously intend. For example, if you intend to play the piano in a concert but you don't practice, it's unlikely you will ever end up on a stage in front of an appreciative audience.

Notice what gets in the way when you want to practice. What is the emotion? What is the little voice telling you? Once you have clarity around that, it is easier to act in alignment with your intentions.

It becomes a matter of creating change towards your goal little by little. Smaller changes are easier to stick with than big ones. In the example above, how can you support yourself to pursue this passion? Is it committing to weekly lessons? Is it setting time aside to play each day? Is it buying a piano? Is it listening to inspiring piano music? Is it having an accountability buddy who checks in with you if you haven't sent them a message saying you practiced today?

Habits

Habits are behaviours we engage in so regularly we don't give them any thought. If this habit is supportive of your dreams and goals, well done! If it is a habit running at cross purposes to your conscious intentions, it is time to realise you have choice in the matter. You always have a choice, even if only in how you respond to a situation.

For example, you might be in the habit of having a cup of coffee in the morning. Do you even like coffee? Does it make you feel good? If so, what is it that makes you feel good? The bitterness, the mix of bitter and sweet, or the kick? Could you get this feeling another way? Just explore. You don't have to do anything about it in the first instance. What other choices are available to you? Tea, herbal or black, juice, water, milk, sleeping in, going for a run? And if coffee is truly your thing, you can now have your cup with a whole new level of appreciation.

Most people don't struggle with their good habits. When you have a habit that doesn't support you, however, examine the uncomfortable emotions, thoughts and beliefs this habit is trying to cover up. The moment before you engage with your habit, stop and breathe for a second. Notice how you feel, and what thoughts are running through your head. Process them. Notice if the compulsion to do your usual habit is still as strong.

The other aspect of breaking a habit is to love something or someone else more than the habit. For example, a lot of women give up smoking and drinking alcohol when they are preparing to fall pregnant or find out they are pregnant. They love the little life forming inside their womb more than the fleeting high of cigarettes or alcohol.

The important aspect is knowing you can choose differently at any given moment. If you know you have choice in one area of your life, you know you have choice in every other area of your life.

Beliefs

I used to sublet a room with a lady whose signature sentence always began, "The reality is...", usually followed by a limiting sentence. I found this puzzling because my reality was nothing like what she described. I told her this, and she went on to declare it might not be true for me because I didn't have children, had a profession, and so on.

Beliefs are probably the trickiest to observe because they are the coloured lens you see everything through. They are so close to the core you don't even know they are there, let alone not set in stone. Again, helpful beliefs are wonderful, "I always land on my feet", "Someone is always around to help when I need it."

The beliefs that limit us are likely to cause most, if not all, our difficulties. Common examples are "I am not good enough", "I am not lovable", "I am a failure", "It's my fault", "It's my responsibility", "I am always the victim" and so on. If you have a version of "I am not good enough", you might not even get started because you aren't going to succeed anyway. Or you might a perfectionist who outperforms all the time. Everyone but you knows this, and many might be tempted to take advantage of it. But you still feel like you don't measure up.

If you believe you are unlovable, you might come across someone who adores the ground you walk on, but you will never notice because you are not receiving at this frequency.

To identify your unhelpful beliefs, notice the sentences you say to yourself or others often or that contain the words 'always' and 'never'. If you have someone who knows and loves you well, ask them about this because when you are in it, you don't have the perspective to see it objectively. Notice your internal reaction to what they say. If you try to defend or justify whenever they point something out, they are probably right on the mark. If you are comfortable with an uncomfortable truth about yourself, you do not feel triggered by it.

If you have become aware of an unhelpful belief, you can repeatedly prove yourself wrong in order to change it. For example, when I was living on a shoestring budget after I started my first business, I gave generously to a busker who played the guitar beautifully. I loved his music and loved giving him money for it as an act of gratitude. It made me feel good, and I proved to myself that I must be abundant if I could afford to give money away like this. It took time, but those tight financial constraints did progressively loosen.

Another strategy is to observe someone who has or does what you would like to be or do. Learn what seems to work for them and practice doing it yourself. If you can, ask that person what strategies they have. Most people are delighted to share. You don't need to re-invent the wheel. That's what role models are for!

"Argue for your limitations, and sure enough, they are yours."

—Richard Bach

Judgement

Often, the trouble arises because we are taught that certain emotions, thoughts, behaviours and habits are unacceptable. As a result, we judge ourselves and others for having these emotions, thoughts, behaviours and habits. We pretend to ourselves and the world that we don't engage with them.

Or if we do, it is an exception and for a very good reason.

The truth is that all, and I mean all, emotions, thoughts and behaviours can be the appropriate response in certain circumstances. By judging them unacceptable, we cut ourselves off from a huge array of experiences and ways of being in the world that are part of the human potential.

The more savagely we suppress and deny these emotions, thoughts and behaviours, the harder these energies push for release, challenging us to acknowledge and accept them. This usually happens at the least opportune moments and can create a lot of hurt, or even harm, in our lives and our relationships.

If we accept and acknowledge the existence of these supposedly unacceptable energies and realize that they might arise in us at times, we can be discerning about when we embody them. We can make a conscious choice about whether we want to play with these energies or not.

"Life is amazing. And then it's awful. And then it's amazing again. And in between the amazing and the awful it's ordinary and mundane and routine. Breathe in the amazing, hold on through the awful, and relax and exhale during the ordinary. That's just living heartbreaking, soul-healing, amazing, awful, ordinary life. And it's breathtakingly beautiful."

—L.R. Knost

Practice
Observing the energies

Emotions, thoughts, behaviours, beliefs and habits are all energy. Each one feels different. Observing them is a crucial part of integrating them and harnessing their power to support your endeavours.

One way to observe them is to describe each one:

- ∞ *What part of your body can you feel it in?*
- ∞ *What does it feel like? (E.g., warm or cold, heavy or light, tingling, stagnant or moving, etc.)*
- ∞ *Does it have a colour?*
- ∞ *Does it have a scent?*
- ∞ *Does it have a voice?*
    - *- What is it saying?*
    - *- Whose voice is it speaking with?*
- ∞ *Is a memory surfacing as you are observing? Why did this memory surface now, and what does it tell you?*

"Whatever you resist you become. If you resist anger, you are always angry. If you resist suffering, you are always suffering. If you resist confusion, you are always confused. We think that we resist certain states because they are there, but they are actually there because we resist them."

—Adyashanti

Suffering is caused by resistance

Our human instinct, when something we perceive as unpleasant comes our way, is to resist it. Our bodies tighten up, our minds slam shut, our hearts close down, we dig our heels in and say, "No! I do not want to be experiencing this right now!"

If you resist it, you feed it energy with your resistance and attention, and hence it grows. What you resist, persists. The more you resist, the more you suffer. What you focus on grows in your awareness. What you allow, flows.

Part of experiencing life on Earth is experiencing unpleasantness and pleasantness. They are energy. The more we resist the energy moving through our bodies and our beings, the more these energies get stuck in our bodies and our energy fields. This causes suffering. This is how many people live stuck in the past, defined by their trauma.

The desire to hang on to pleasant and desirable states of being is equally problematic. They also need to move through your body and energy field. If you try to prolong your highs, you are still looking outside to feel good instead of finding the permanent spring of joy and love you carry in your heart. If you are connected to your heart, you can notice both the pleasant and the unpleasant, and gather and use the information they offer, knowing your happiness does not depend on what goes on around you.

Think of Miss Havisham from Charles Dickens' "*Great Expectations*" who was left at the altar on her wedding day. She didn't allow herself to move on from that moment. She could have lived a life of joy and love had she chosen not to allow that one moment to define her.

Try this with physical pain: sink into it, detach from the idea that this is pain and feel it as just a sensation. Notice how the experience of the pain shifts. This technique makes the difference between a painful and an ecstatic childbirth. If it works for that, it will work for a scraped knee.

When you are in emotional pain, try to feel into the emotions and what they are telling you. Notice the quality of the energy present in your body and what it requires of you to process it: I feel sad because a chapter of my life is coming to an end. My body needs to cry. I feel angry because someone crossed a boundary. It's time to reinforce that boundary. I feel joyful because I am in nature and can feel the sun on my skin. I am going to sing to express it or I am going to lie in the grass and just feel it all.

Life moves through you. Life offers you highs and lows of emotions and experiences. If you allow them to move through your body and energy fields without resistance or judgement, you can ride these waves of life like an expert surfer. If you remember to breathe deeply when an unpleasant experience comes your way and allow your body to express the attendant emotions, they will only be there for a short period of time. Then the next wave can pick you up and carry you along.

Allow Life to flow through you.

You might experience yourself as a human being experiencing Life, but you are Life experiencing itself through you in equal measure. Life is curious about everything and judges nothing. If you allow experiences, emotions and thoughts to move through you, you can live from a place of Life happening *for* you rather than *to* you.

This is what is meant by the concept of 'detachment'.

"Sit with it.

Sit with it.

Sit with it.

Sit with it.

Even though you want to run.

Even when it's heavy and difficult.

Even if you are not quite sure of the way through.

Healing happens by feeling."

—Dr. Rebecca Ray

Dis-ease as the body's call for help

Why is all this important? If you continuously resist, ignore, bury or deny the unpleasant energies trying to pass through your energy field and body, they build up.

To start with, the unpleasant or undesirable energy feels like discomfort and is relatively easy to process. The longer you ignore it, the denser the energy becomes. Every time you encounter a triggering situation that you suppress, you add another layer to the energy. Being triggered is an opportunity to feel into what is going on and to process this energy.

The longer you ignore it, the more likely it is to become a disease in the physical body.

For example, the day after the first time I stood up in front of an audience and told them how the world works according to my understanding, I developed a quinsy. This is a swelling of the lymphatic tissue at the back of the throat that can be fatal if it cuts off the airways. This quinsy was so bad I couldn't eat for a week and had difficulties breathing because only a third of my airway was open.

I had done public speaking before, and this had never happened. But on previous occasions, I had always spoken in my role as a professional and experienced practitioner. This time, I was presenting myself in my most authentic and vulnerable way. It was my body's way of drawing my attention to a fear of speaking out.

I'd had quinsy before, but never this badly, and it had always resolved itself quickly. I haven't had one since.

I have since come across several other people who had sore throats after they stood up and spoke about something they were passionate or vulnerable about for the first time.

Dis-ease draws our attention to what we have buried so deeply that we don't know we don't know. When you acknowledge discomfort consciously, you know there is something you don't know. But the deep-seated core fears or issues that pervade and colour your life without your knowing can be so agonisingly uncomfortable you would do almost anything to avoid feeling, processing or integrating them. If that goes on long enough, this energy eventually becomes so insistent and dense it can show up as physical disease that we cannot avoid any more.

Happiness versus growth mindset

In our society, we are obsessed with happiness, physical beauty and youth. We are told daily that if we aren't happy and young, we are failing at life. Just look at the average advertisement!

However, if you keep obsessing about youth, you become stagnant and miss out on fully experiencing all the offerings that come with each different life stage. If you keep obsessing about happiness, you set yourself up for failure because Life moves in cycles. If you aren't prepared to plumb the depths of your potential, you are equally unable to soar to its heights.

What if you move your focus from happiness to growth? In that mindset, pleasant experiences are appreciated, and unpleasant ones are considered gifts in strange wrapping paper that Life offers to encourage you to step into the next most magnificent version of yourself.

Unpleasant experiences contribute to growth and are likely the ones you will be most grateful for down the track. They give you deeper insights and get you closer to the magnificent, beautiful core of your own being. This encourages you to remain open in difficult times because you know if you persevere, you will find that diamond in amongst all the muck, and it will have been so worth it. It builds character and develops resilience.

In this mindset, happiness is a by-product because you don't resist the difficult, challenging or painful experiences coming your way, and hence you don't get stuck in them.

"The deeper that sorrow carves into your being, the more joy you can contain. Is not the cup that holds your wine the very cup that was burned in the potter's oven? And is not the lute that soothes your Spirit, the very wood that was hollowed with knives?"

—Kahil Gibran, the Prophet, *"On joy and sorrow"*

Communicating with your body

Why is it important to process your emotions and thoughts, and to examine what underlies your behaviours and habits?

When you are carried away with emotions or thoughts, you are not paying attention to your body. At best, your energy is present from your eyes and above. At worst, your energy is outside your body altogether.

Sometimes I look into a person's eyes but feel confused. I feel like their energy field is not aligned with their body and I should be looking at them off to one side. Have you ever experienced that?

The best analogy I can think of is the movie *"Click"* with Adam Sandler, where he is given a remote for his life, and he fast forwards through all the unpleasant and boring parts. The result is he does not truly live his life, or have deep connection or involvement with those he loves.

Thankfully, the body can function without you, at least for a period of time.

But if you resist the energies that are passing like clouds on a starry night by not feeling your body, they cannot dissipate. Your body needs you to be present for and feel what is going on in your body and your energy field to allow these clouds to dissolve. By being absent from your body, these energies get stuck in your body or energy field. They become denser and denser, and more and more unpleasant, which in turn makes you flee your body more often. The result may well become sickness of some type. This is the body's cry for help. If you take medication to make the symptoms away, you are still not processing. Instead, you are driving the dysfunction deeper, until such time they can no longer be ignored.

Know that *all* humans have access to *all* emotions. Know that you have a choice in how you translate the energy of the emotions and thoughts into beliefs and behaviours.

You may feel that your body being unwell or sick is punishment. But sickness is usually the consequence of how you have been interacting with your body. It wants to be well. The cells in your body love you in the same way we love nature. Your body wants to thrive. All you have to do is to give it the resources it needs to be able to do this. All you have to do is to be attentive to the signal your body gives you when things are going awry and needs your conscious help to regain balance. Then act accordingly. Love your body back.

This video is profound: Dying to be me! by Anita Moorjani at TEDxBayArea

https://www.youtube.com/watch?v=rhcJNJbRJ6U

"Your body knows, it will literally tell you when it is time to move onto a new chapter in your life. Trust it."

—Thoughts Wonder

Practice
Communicating with your body

Put your hands on the part of your body trying to get your attention with symptoms. Give it gratitude for all the ways it has been trying to serve you, even if, or especially if, you don't understand why it is doing what it is doing.

Ask it questions:

- ∞ *What do you need me to know right now?*
- ∞ *What do you need from me?*
- ∞ *Is there a memory of the first time this came up?*

Allow whatever needs to arise to come up. This is a magical process. Trust that you will not get more to deal with than you can handle at any given moment.

Interviews with women about communication with their bodies

How does your body communicate with you?
Have you had physical sensations or illnesses that gave you new levels of insight?

Megan:

My body is everything. She is the vessel for my connection with Earth and with God and everything in between. She is where I experience all that life has to offer. She is how I process my emotions and she is my guidance system for knowing my truth. She is my livelihood and how I work with my clients. My body is a space of creation, of birthing and she is always leading me into new ways of being.

I recently had a skin cancer that required surgery and three months of radiation. Even more recently I have been experiencing fibromyalgia symptoms. Geez, not so sure I am the best person for this book!!!

My body speaks to me loud and clear. She will scream at me if I am not living in alignment and honouring her in a way she deserves and desires.

My chronic pain healed completely, but still, every four years or so, my lower back becomes painful for no logical or physical reason. It literally stops me. I have traced this back to a karmic pattern and usually happens when I am uplevelling in my life or business.

Beckie:

I've had dermatitis appear on the top of my middle finger on my right (dominant) hand when I needed to put boundaries in place and tell certain people to f**k off. I've also had a lack of boundaries show up in skin breakouts. I've had a fear of being pregnant and childbirth show up as irregular periods.

Being diagnosed with an autoimmune disease when I was in my late twenties was one of the greatest blessings I've had. It sent me on a path of deep self-discovery and learning of the (medical) systems we live amongst and that there is a whole other world of truth and healing available to us.

Prue:

My body responds to what I feed and water it with. It will let me know if the food I gave it was light or dense. I get this reading from my energy levels about my activities, who I hang out with and what information I consume.

I experience universal 'truth' or recognition through tingles in my physical body. I experience knowingness and intuition by way of my body too. It's what guides my life and my work.

Diane:

My body communicates *all* the time. Often through pain, for example, headaches when I have been on the computer too much, cellulitis when I don't move enough and tiredness when I work too hard. These days I am much better at listening too.

As a child, I had terrible tonsillitis all the time, maybe three times in an English winter. I realised much later in life that it was because I never felt safe expressing myself and there was no one to express to anyway as my parents were workaholics.

My thyroid needed to be removed in my 30s and I realised it was because I still wasn't speaking my absolute truth. I was trying to please people. I did a stocktake and went back through my life. I realised how many times I had been between two opposing people, for example, my mum and my dad; my dad and my brother; my parents and my husband; my mother and my son, and so forth. On and on it went. It didn't help that I am a Libran who thrives on balance and absolutely detests upsets. I am determined to never keep my words inside me and to always speak my truth. I healed my thyroid without surgery using an energetic medicine machine.

Iris:

My body speaks loudly and clearly. The canary in the coalmine for me is a headache. Whenever something is awry, that is how I am prodded to address it.

I gave up gluten well over a decade ago. Until then, I always felt tired after eating and thought that was normal. After about three or four years of being gluten free, it became possible to buy gummi bears where I live in Australia. These were my favourite sweets when I was a kid, so I bought a pack and ended up eating about three-quarters of it in one sitting. The next day I got a migraine. I didn't put two and two together until the same thing happened about three weeks later. I checked the ingredients list and saw they were made with wheat syrup and contained gluten.

Needless to say, spending a day with a migraine is far too high a price to pay for a handful of moments of chewy sweetness. I haven't eaten any more gummi bears since!

There are other, more delicate, signs too. Goosebumps when I speak a new spiritual truth. Tears in my eyes when I am deeply connected and moved. Deep sighs when I get too wound up. Unpleasant tingling on my skin when I need to sleep.

Practice
Giving your body love and gratitude

If this is difficult, start with a part of you that's easy to love. Maybe give your hands gratitude and love for their cleverness at cooking a meal or earning a living. Maybe give your eyes love and gratitude for the gift of sight. Maybe give your feet love and gratitude for the gift of walking. Or give gratitude to your heart for beating, giving you life and the ability to love.

Maybe you already appreciate some part of your body: the beautiful shape of your lips, or the lovely glow of your skin. Whatever it is, quietly tune into the beauty of this part of your body. Notice how this part feels different after you have appreciated it. You will notice, in whichever way you notice these things, that the energy of that part is more vibrant. As you get better at this practice, add another body part, and another, until eventually you love your whole body just as it is.

You can use the "yoga nidra gratitude meditation" on my YouTube channel https://www.youtube.com/@irisangellys to help with this process. Notice how your body feels before and after the practice.

ALGORITHM OR
HUMANITY?

A contemporary philosopher, who shall remain unnamed, feels that trans-humanism is the next step for humanity. The basic idea seems to be that by fusing our minds with the internet, algorithms can calculate what our preferences are, know us better than we know ourselves, and then proceed to provide us with whatever it is we want, desire or crave.

His example is that had he been subject to an algorithm, he would have known at 16 rather than at 21 that he was gay. The inference is that it would have saved him a lot of struggles and heartache.

But it also takes the human experience out of having a human experience. Remember the last time you did a 1,000-piece puzzle, learnt a new skill, went to a new place or discovered the most delightful food, landscapes, hiking trail or massage therapist? It is the *process* that gives life excitement, meaning and a sense of fulfillment when you have achieved or experienced something new and enriching.

If you are given a 1,000-piece puzzle and only have to put in the last piece, it isn't satisfying because the effort that went into assembling the first 999 pieces isn't yours. If you could download the software to know how to play an instrument perfectly, you would never experience the thrill of noticing your progress and tackling increasingly difficult pieces along the way. If you could climb Mount Everest without getting off the lounge for a year prior, you wouldn't get that deep sense of achievement of doing something so difficult it was considered impossible not too long ago.

Heartache and struggle refine us and soften the hard edges of our humanness. We get to experience the sense of fulfillment and joy when we have overcome our struggles and heartache. It is not accidental that many teenagers see the world in black and white, whereas older people see the world in shades of grey, or even colour. They have been in situations where there was no ideal outcome and lived with the consequences of the choices made at that time.

If humans do hook themselves into an algorithm, they will become pleasure addicts, unable to cope if the satellite or the electricity fails. You would escape your body even more. You would become even more disconnected from people you love. To me, that is a bleak prospect indeed.

En-lighten-ment

Have you ever travelled from A to B, and had no recollection of the journey when you arrived? You spent the time thinking about something other than the path you were travelling. You didn't actually experience your journey.

Similarly, most people live their lives 'outside' their bodies. Their attention is focused on their thoughts or emotions. They are not paying attention to what is happening in their bodies.

People like this come across as being ungrounded, overly emotional or intellectual, anxious, day-dreamy or not present in other ways.

While this is going on, your bodies valiantly relies on its innate intelligence to keep going as well as possible under the circumstances, devoid of loving attention from you.

Once you decide to reconnect and allow yourself to feel what's going on in your body and your energy field, this attention starts evaporating the clouds obscuring your view of the night sky. The clouds disappear, the sky clears and the view becomes ever more stunningly beautiful. Your body starts feeling like a nice place to be present in. Your body becomes lighter. The more you do this process, the more en-lighten-ment you feel.

In our society, we are under the impression that to attain enlightenment, we need to retire to a distant cave or monastery and meditate for 20 hours a day. In our not-so-distant past, people would 'mortify the flesh' and physically harm their bodies to become 'pure'.

The irony is the instrument to attain en-lighten-ment is embracing everything your human experience offers. Be truly present in your body. Pay attention to what is going on right here and right now. Accept what is going on. Make conscious choices about how to respond. In that state of clarity, go about your day. Derive joy from small, mundane things like cooking dinner, going for a walk or having a shower. As a result, everything around you will start to reveal its inherent magic.

Enlightenment is not found by trying to escape this 'mortal coil', but by whole-heartedly saying, "*Yes!*" to everything it has to offer.

The bigger picture

How we, as a society, treat our bodies is a direct reflection of how we treat Mother Earth. Many of us see our bodies as a tool to make us feel pleasure and our Earth as a resource to provide us with whatever we want. We take without thought for the consequence to ourselves or other beings.

If you can treat your body as an intelligent entity with its own needs and wants, with its own desire for joy, care and love, as an equal partner in this adventure called 'human being lifetime', you will start seeing Earth and all her creatures in the same way.

Imagine living a life basking in the inherent beauty of your body and of Mother Earth.

Welcome to New Earth.

The future I see

The future I see
Is gentle
Forests are lush
The world's waters are crystal clear
And sparkling
And teeming with life
Deserts bloom

The future I see
Is kind
Humans have rediscovered their mission as tenders of the garden
Every human footstep caresses and massages the Earth
Every human heart beats with gratitude for being alive

The future I see
Is loving
Humans have rediscovered that the primary purpose for hands
Is to caress the animals, the plants, the rocks, the loam
And each other
And for taking a thorn out of a paw
Hands are also good for expressing creatively
The joy and reverence for Life

The future I see
Is joyous
The sounds are of the natural world
And of human voices singing and laughing with delight
And some humans sing with the whales and dolphins
Of the joys of the deep ocean

The future I see
Is light
Humans nourish themselves with light and air and water and love and
    Earth's bounty
Generously given and gratefully accepted

The future I see
Is reverent
Every being, mineral, plant, animal, human or etheric
Is treated with reverence and gratitude for that entity's unique gift
And contribution
Humans and animals of all kinds are friends,
Enjoying the richness of experience that friendship brings

The future I see
Is ecstatic
New human beings are invited into the world consciously and birthed in
ecstasy
Remembering the oneness of all

The future I see
Is full of gratitude
I see myself, sitting on the Earth, helping restore balance by helping water
flow here
And encouraging a plant to grow there
And sending some nurturing love to a nest yonder
And slowly, sparklingly, vibrating out of existence
Because my work here is done

"You don't have to move mountains. Simply fall in love with life. Be a tornado of happiness, gratitude and acceptance. You will change the world just by being a warm, kind-hearted human being."

—Anita Krizzan

Interviews with women about their relationships with their bodies

Describe your journey from numbness or disliking your body to liking your body. Is there a particular reason why you didn't like your body? What did you feel like back then? How did you get to a place where you do like your body? What does your relationship with your body feel like now? How have your beliefs about your body, yourself, your relationships and your world changed?

Megan:

15 years ago, my whole world changed after I slipped on a milkshake and landed directly on my knee. The next two years became a whirlwind of medical appointments, operations, spinal blocks, chronic pain and medications until I was eventually labelled with an eleven percent disability for life by the mainstream medical world.

It was a lot to take in for someone who had hardly been to the doctor in her life and had never even broken a bone. All the physical ailments snowballed out of control. My sore knee turned into chronic pain, freezing feet, slipped discs in my back, neck pain and deteriorating mental health.

It took a toll on my whole body, mind and soul. It affected my life in every aspect. Before this I was a runner. That was my outlet: my meditation and my exercise. Before this, I loved my job as a Youth Practitioner. Before this, I was happy in my relationships. I had an active full life.

After this, I became a shadow of myself.

It affected my capacity to work, my mental health, my social wellbeing and living to my full potential. While I was journeying with the effects of physical pain, the doctors never discussed my emotions and the relationship trauma I was experiencing simultaneously.

Life as I knew it fell apart. The relationship I was in broke down. The house I was living in was no longer my home. My financial situation changed. Things I once enjoyed and brought me pleasure were no longer possible. Practical things like driving, going to the office and even having conversations were affected by my pain and lack of movement in my leg.

There was so much grief for these things as well as the letting go of who I was. My capacity to deal with life diminished. I was a shadow of my easy-go-happy self. I was depressed, in pain, lost, alone and confused. I cried many oceans worth of tears. I was stuck in the "Why me? What have I done to deserve this!"

I hated my body because it was full of pain and didn't function to its full potential. I put on weight which gave me another reason to not like it. I even went as far as getting a breast reduction to ease the pain. My body was poked and prodded by many physicians. I took medications that made me so drowsy I couldn't get out of bed for days. I was told over and over again that my pain was all in my head. I was accused of doctor-hopping and making it all up. Often, I was put in the too hard basket.

One day I was assessed by a medical team, and they told me I would never walk without a limp and declared I would have an eleven per cent disability for life. That was the day I said ENOUGH!!

I started seeking alternative paths. I followed the signs. I saw a yoga poster on a lamppost. I went. I fell in love with it, and I cried. My friend was a kinesiologist. I booked an appointment and the only way I can explain this is that I experienced a miracle. I walked in as a broken woman, and I walked out, three hours later, as a woman full of understanding, hope and trust in my journey.

I found my soul path. Everything began to make sense and fall into place. I learnt how to get out of my head and into my body to process my thoughts and feel my emotions. I left my job and studied kinesiology. I found myself. I got to know myself deeply, all parts, even the dark ugly parts. I cleared out all the trauma from my body. I found new and more aligned friendships. I found my soulful self and I love her.

Beckie:
Growing up, I was never the pretty girl, the skinny girl or the little, petite, cute girl at school. Although I was never overweight

as a child, I was always a bigger build and still am.

I remember comparing myself to other girls at school, in particular my thighs and legs. In Year 7, I would wrap wide sticky tape around my body, especially my stomach and thighs, to make them appear slimmer under clothing. I always wanted to be able to show my belly in my early teens as low waist jeans and crop tops were in fashion back then, but I never felt like I had the body to do so.

I got my belly button pierced for my thirteenth birthday thinking that along with being 'cool', it would make my belly look better, but in my mind it didn't. It just became something I had that no one saw until later in my teens.

I was the youngest of three girls and our mum was always a small and slim build. Us three girls are built more like our dad. I, in particular, am built the same as my nan, my mother's mum. I remember wishing I had my mum's build when I was a child and early teenager. I always wondered if people looked as us three girls and thought maybe we didn't belong to my mum because we were all so much bigger builds than her. My dad, although quite a stocky build, isn't tall at all whereas my middle sister and I are.

I remember reading a Dolly or Girlfriend magazine when I was about twelve. Someone wrote in asking why one of their breasts was larger than the other and if it were normal. I remember that moment so clearly and how fearful I became of that happening to me. It would be so embarrassing if something were wrong with me. I believe this was my first lesson in the power of manifestation and what we focus on because from the moment my breasts started to develop, the right one was a good cup size larger, and still is. Until recent years, I was always *so* self-conscious about this and hated a male seeing my breasts in the light. Feeling them with one hand on each would be an easy opportunity for him to realise they were not the same size. It's only in recent years I have learnt to love and accept my breasts.

When I was 17, I found myself in a terrible situation which resulted in me falling pregnant and having an abortion. Since then, I held so much fear around becoming pregnant again that I avoided this natural progression for many years. I knew I wanted to have children one day and straight after getting married I found out I was pregnant. We weren't trying as such, but I did know when I was ovulating. I hadn't used any form of contraception for seven years though I tracked my cycle.

I didn't think one time would eventuate into anything, but it did. Looking back, I can see the magic and intention with that love-making session and the gifts of self-discovery and healing that followed during my pregnancy, birth and into motherhood with our daughter.

In the lead-up to becoming pregnant, I lived an incredibly fun but self-destructive and unhealthy lifestyle. Weekends were filled with social events that meant a lot of excessive drinking, smoking and occasionally cocaine use. Although I had so much fun, I also knew it wasn't healthy and that I was suppressing something I didn't want to face. But until I became pregnant, I didn't know what that was.

The day I found out I was pregnant, my whole life and lifestyle changed. I withdrew from my social circles, not only because I wasn't out drinking and partying, but because I needed to contract to heal and move forward into the next phase of my life. Although I felt terrified of what was ahead of me, I knew it was what I wanted.

My journey through pregnancy allowed me to fall in love with my body in a way I'd never experienced before. The more pregnant I looked, the more beautiful and sexier I felt. I felt incredibly feminine, soft, and magical and relaxed into my femininity more than ever before. This allowed my husband to step into his masculinity more and together we found more balance within our relationship.

Since giving birth and the months that have passed, I still feel deep love and appreciation for my body. I have a few stretch marks on my now softer belly, and I continue to massage beautiful oil onto my stomach like I did during pregnancy. I still feel those loving feelings towards my body when doing so.

I truly believe the universe knows what it's doing and the timing of everything in our lives is perfect. This is the case with the changes I needed to make in my life, the healing I'd been avoiding and the next chapter of my life I was holding myself back from. All this happened from the arrival of our daughter.

Prue:

My relationship with my body for a long time was merely physical, based on appearance and shaped by what others, the media or society might think was healthy or beautiful.

For a long time, I rejected my body, how it looked and how it felt. I felt quite numb physically and emotionally or I would take measures to numb it through food and alcohol.

The journey to me fully appreciating my body has come alongside my journey of understanding and accepting all of who I am and all parts of me: physical, mental, emotional, spiritual, multidimensional.

The shift for me truly has been about understanding that my body is the way that I get to experience, via the senses, all that this world has to offer. I'm a feeler over being a thinker, so I sense things through my body. It's how the world and spirit talk to me and how I perceive those messages.

It's actually kind of magical and without my body, that communication wouldn't be possible.

I'm not going to lie. There are still times when I wish I could snap my fingers and be in triathlon-shape but I have given up hating on my body. My relationship now is one of gratitude, appreciation, honour and respect.

My perception shifts are as follows:

Body – My body has shifted from a one-dimensional perspective to a multidimensional portal and transmission device, both sending out and receiving.

Self – My beliefs have shifted from feeling unworthy and fearful of taking up space to trusting that I have a purpose and that I will take up exactly the right amount of space.

Relationships – I am aware that when people are receiving me, they are receiving so much more than just my body. They are receiving energy, light, emotions and sensations.

World – In the simplest terms, my beliefs have shifted from life happening to me to life happening for me, from limitation to possibility.

Diane:

I was always told I was 'fat' as a child and I hated myself. I was embarrassed and spent at least half my life, if not three quarters of it, on some diet or eating regime. One day, I realised that my body is actually *not* who I am. It may be what people see, but I am way more than that. I am many, many things. While I do not have a skinny body, my body was cherished, loved and adored by my beautiful husband, and I learned to love it too. He loved its curves and softness and I do too.

Is there a particular reason why you didn't like your body?
Mum said I was fat, and she couldn't find jodhpurs to fit me!!!

What did you feel like back then?
Small, insignificant, wrong and that I didn't fit.

How did you get to a place where you do like your body?

I realised how much time I had wasted attempting to look different from what I have always looked. I also realised many moons ago that I had taken on my father's body shape because he adored and loved me whereas my mother was beautiful, slim and I didn't feel love from her at all.

What does your relationship with your body feel like now?

It feels like an old friend, with its scars, its facial lines, its belly and its thighs and I love it.

How have your beliefs about your body, yourself, your relationships, your world changed?

I am less inhibited, more free to be me and less concerned about what people think. I have many friends who love me the way I am. I thought, if they can do that, why wouldn't I choose to do it also?

Iris:

I am lucky because I have always liked my body. When I was young, I stood out because I was very close to the beauty ideal of the time. I lived in Spain from 10 to 19 years old, and being tall, blonde and blue-eyed made me stand out in the crowd and marked me as definitely not a local. As a result, I got far too much and too intense male attention, and I never felt safe unless I had a male protector with me.

I was very smart and did well at school, which also set me apart and isolated me.

As a result, I came out of my teenage years feeling like I didn't belong. I didn't want to be on the planet. I was a vegetarian and very underweight, which I now understand was a subconscious attempt at vanishing, to get away from all the discomfort I was feeling.

When I was 26, someone induced me to eat chicken for the first time in 12 years and my body loved it! I had effectively been starving it of the nutrients it needed, and I couldn't get enough. With it came the commitment to staying on the planet and working through what I needed to process.

Through all of this, I never disliked my body. At 14, I decided I would never smoke, do drugs or drink, which I stuck with. It seems very grown up and insightful for a 14-year-old to make those kinds of decisions.

My relationship with my body is now one of respect and care. I love doing things that make it feel good: yoga, singing, resting, playing guitar, playing in water, eating beautiful food. I also love how it feels after I have shifted some heavy energy.

"You are enough just being who you are. Anything you do is a bonus."

—Iris Angellys, *Passion to Thrive*

Interviews with women about who they are

Who are you?

I am deeply grateful to Megan, Beckie, Prue and Diane for their contributions to this book. I am blessed to have such insightful, authentic and brilliant friends. Each one of these women is making a huge difference in the world, and I am in awe of each one of them.

Megan:
Megan Johnston – Soul Medicine Woman...
https://www.meganjohnston.com.au

Beckie:
Beckie Stevenson. Business Owner. Wife. Mum. Truth Seeker and Speaker.

Prue:
My name's Prue Blennerhassett. I'm an intuitive business strategist and women's transformation catalyst, living and loving on the East Coast of Australia, just out of Byron Bay. https://ceopriestess.com

Diane:
I am a woman of passion and determination, love and joy. I have lived a life of extraordinary experiences that have all added up, good and bad, to make me who I am today. I live in a state of grace and gratefulness for all I have around me, my family, my friends, my beautiful sanctuary of a home, my treasures, the ocean, the sky, the stars, sunsets and sunrises. https://beyondtheordinary.net.au

References and Additional Reading

Emoto, Masaru: https://masaru-emoto.net/ https://www.emotopeaceproject.net/water-crystal-gallery

Hay, Louise. 1984. *You Can Heal Your Life*. Hay House.

Moorjani, Anita. 2013. *Dying to be me!* TEDxBayArea https://www.youtube.com/watch?v=rhcJNJbRJ6U

Pert, Candace. 1999. *Molecules of Emotion: The Science Behind Mind-Body Medicine.* Simon & Schuster.

YouTube: Iris Angellys
https://www.youtube.com/channel/UC715fwBNcK_iwWQbDJ-PAgg

Quote sources

"Argue for your limitations, and sure enough, they are yours."
Richard Bach, 1977 "Illusions, the adventures of a Reluctant Messiah" Chapter 7

"We are mosaics – pieces of light, love, history, stars – glued together with magic and music and words."
Anita Krizzan
https://www.goodreads.com/quotes/1183871-we-are-mosaics-pieces-of-light-love-history-stars-glued

"There are only two ways to live your life.
One is as though nothing is a miracle.
The other is as though everything is a miracle."
Albert Einstein
https://www.goodreads.com/quotes/987-there-are-only-two-ways-to-live-your-life-one

"The moment you change your perception is the moment you rewrite the chemistry in your body"
Bruce H. Lipton
https://www.brucelipton.com/about/

"You may consider yourself an individual.
But as a cell biologist I can tell you that you are in truth a cooperative community of approximately fifty trillion single-celled citizens."
Bruce H. Lipton
https://www.brucelipton.com/what-do-you-think-will-be-significant-the-future/

"I am because we are."
"A person is a person through
other people."
Source unknown, Ubuntu Philosophy
https://en.wikipedia.org/wiki/Ubuntu_philosophy

"Today I asked my body what she needed,
Which is a big deal
Considering my journey of
Not really asking that much.
I thought she might need more water.
Or proteins.
Or greens.
Or yoga.
Or supplements.
Or movement.
But as I stood in the shower
Reflecting on her stretch marks,
Her roundness where I would like flatness,
Her softness where I would prefer firmness,
All those conditioned wishes
That form a bundle of
Never-Quite-Right-Ness,
She whispered very gently:
Could you just love me like this?"
Hollie Holden
Facebook – Hollie Holden – Notes on Living & Loving 30 June 2016

"Intuition: When you don't know How you know... But you know you
know... and you know you knew and that's all you needed to know."
Zen to Zany
Facebook – Poetry of Kat t 27 February 2021

"There are two types of tired, I suppose.
One is a dire need of sleep.
The other is a dire need for peace."
Mandeq Ahmed
https://themindsjournal.com/there-are-two-types-of-tired/

"Now, every time I witness a strong person, I want to know: What dark
did you conquer in your story?
Mountains don't happen without earthquakes."
Katherine MacKenett
Facebook – Katherine MacKenett Writer 22 August 2021

"It takes courage to say yes to rest and play in a culture where exhaustion
is seen as a status symbol."
Brenée Brown
Facebook – Simply + Fiercely 21 September 2022

"Rest is not idle, it is not wasteful. Sometimes rest is the most productive
thing you can do for body and soul."
Erica Layne
https://ericalayne.co/7-ways-to-accept-and-lean-into-a-season-of-
rest/rest-is-not-idle-2/

"The whole world is a series of miracles, but we are so used to them we call
them ordinary things."
Hans Christian Andersen
https://www.goodreads.com/quotes/324050-the-whole-world-is-a-
series-of-miracles-but-we-re

"The cure for anything is salt water: sweat, tears or the sea"
Karen Blixen (Isak Dinesen), 1934 "Seven Gothic Tales – The Deluge
at Norderney"

"We're not saying you should take 42 percent of your time to rest; we're saying if you don't take the 42 percent, the 42 percent will take you. It will grab you by the face, shove you to the ground, put its foot on your chest, and declare itself the victor."
Emily Nagoski, 2019 "Burnout: The Secret to Unlocking the Stress Cycle"

"If you feel something calling you to dance or write or paint or sing, please refuse to worry about whether you are good enough. Just do it."
Glennon Doyle
Facebook – Contemplative Monk 3 June 2021

"Piglet noticed that even though he had a Very Small Heart, it could hold a very large amount of Gratitude."
A. A. Milne, 1926 "Winnie-the-Pooh"

"Travelling through life with curiosity rather than judgement is how one finds the magic in each moment."
Erin Chatters
Facebook – Erin Chatters Inspires 1 February 2022

"I am not the calm before the storm. I am both the calm and the storm."
Ivy Atalanta
Pinterest – Enie

"In Irish, when you talk about emotion, you don't say "I am sad". You'd say "Sadness is on me" –'Ta bron orm'.
And I love that because there's an implication of not identifying yourself with the emotion fully. I am not sad, it's just that sadness is on me for a while. Something else will be on me another time, and that's a good thing to recognise."
P. O. Tuama
Facebook – Esoteric Eye 1 September 2022

"That was the thing about thoughts. They thought themselves, and then dropped into your head in the hope that you would think so too."
Terry Pratchett, 2010 "I Shall Wear Midnight" Chapter 4

"Argue for your limitations, and sure enough, they are yours."
Richard Bach, 1977 "Illusions, the adventures of a Reluctant Messiah" Chapter 7

"Life is amazing. And then it's awful. And then it's amazing again. And in between the amazing and the awful it's ordinary and mundane and routine. Breathe in the amazing, hold on through the awful, and relax and exhale during the ordinary. That's just living heartbreaking, soul-healing, amazing, awful, ordinary life. And it's breathtakingly beautiful."
L.R. Knost
Facebook – L.R.Knost - Little Hearts/Gentle Parenting Resources 22 March 2020

"Whatever you resist you become. If you resist anger, you are always angry. If you resist suffering, you are always suffering. If you resist confusion, you are always confused. We think that we resist certain states because they are there, but they are actually there because we resist them."
Adyashanti
Facebook – Dolores Cannon 16 March 2022

"Sit with it.
Sit with it.
Sit with it.
Sit with it.
Even though you want to run.
Even when it's heavy and difficult.
Even if you are not quite sure of the way through.
Healing happens by feeling."
Rebecca Ray
Facebook – Soul Sisters Memorial Foundation 29 May 2022

"The deeper that sorrow carves into your being, the more joy you can contain. Is not the cup that holds your wine the very cup that was burned in the potter's oven? And is not the lute that soothes your spirit, the very wood that was hollowed with knives?"
Kahil Gibran, 1923 "The Prophet"

"Your body knows, it will literally tell you when it is time to move onto a new chapter in your life. Trust it."
Thoughts Wonder
Facebook – The Life and Adventures of Raven 7 April

"You don't have to move mountains. Simply fall in love with life.
Be a tornado of happiness, gratitude and acceptance.
You will change the world just by being a warm, kind-hearted human being."
Anita Krizzan
Facebook – Anita Krizzan 7 November 2022

"You are enough just being who you are.
Anything you do is a bonus."
Iris Angellys, 2020 "Passion to Thrive"

Acknowledgements

I am grateful to you, dear reader—for taking the leap of reading this book, and for wanting to be the best version of you that you can be, and for wanting to make a difference in the world.

I have been so blessed with a beautiful, supportive team that have made the creation and publishing of this book a joyful and delightful experience. I am deeply grateful to my editor Rananda Rich, from the Ink Rat, to my publisher, Natasha Gilmour, from The Kind Press, and to Sarah K Jones, my website magician.

Thank you, Kerstin Gruebmeye, for giving me the title for this book.

I am also deeply grateful to the women who have taken the time to share their experiences for this book: Kate Connolly, Megan Johnson, Beckie Stevenson, Prue Blennerhassett and Diane McCann. All of you have had a profound effect on my life and I feel blessed to know you.

I am grateful to my husband, who supports me unconditionally in my diverse endeavours of varying degrees of craziness, and who is happy for me to take up all the wall spaces available with my art.

I am grateful to my parents, who gave me a varied, interesting and challenging upbringing. I appreciate this more and more as I get older.

I am grateful to all my female friends, long term and short term. You know who you are, and I am grateful for all the love, support and wisdom you have showered me with over the years. I am grateful for my male friends, who model such a different way of being in the world.

I am grateful for all the patients who have come to me for support with their health, you have taught me so much. And I am grateful for my amazing staff, whose support is so crucial.

And I am grateful for Mother Earth and the Universe for being able to have this crazy and intense and joyous and adventuresome experience of being a human.

Blessings.

Resources

How to connect with me!

To deepen your connection with yourself even further, I invite you to check out the self-assessment **quiz** and **online course** created to complement this book:

Quiz: https://www.irisangellys.com/quiz

Online Course: https://www.irisangellys.com/program-welcome

For courses or personal sessions
Website: irisangellys.com

For lots of free meditations, podcasts and poems
YouTube: @irisangellys

For workshop announcements and inspirational material
Facebook: Passion to Thrive

Also available for purchase, the beautiful Archetypal Artwork greeting cards from the book. You can delight someone with a gift, or you can use them as guidance cards, as they have affirmations on the front. Each card was created with the energy of the affirmation, so you can use them to tune in to that energy also, in meditation or otherwise.
Visit, irisangellys.com

About the Author

Iris Angellys is an author, artist, mentor, healer, workshop facilitator, chiropractor and applied kinesiologist. Her writing is based on a combination of her own lived experience and insights she has gained from seeing over twenty-five thousand patients after nearly thirty years of practice. Iris has a deep passion to empower people to thrive in their lives and bodies, so they can offer the world the gift of their unique soul frequency.

Within the pages of her first book *Passion to Thrive* (Balboa Press), Iris introduces different archetypes that guide us through difficult situations and circumstances back to our own magnificent selves and to the divine feminine.

Iris lives with her husband and beautiful dog Jasper on the North Coast of NSW, Australia.